Programming For ENGINEERS ...in True BASIC

By

Avery Catlin

True BASIC Press

1996

Programming for ENGINEERS ...in True BASIC

By
Avery Catlin

Published by True BASIC Inc. Printed in the United States of America

ISBN 0-939553-35-X

True BASIC, Inc.
12 Commerce Avenue
West Lebanon, NH 03784-1669 USA

Web Address: http://www.truebasic.com
Sales Phone: 800 436-2111 or 603 298-8517
24-hr Fax: 603 298-7015

Contents

PREFACE

Programming for Engineers... in True BASIC is written for undergraduate engineering students in their first year. It assumes no previous experience in computer programming. It is also a suitable book for students who have taken an earlier programming course but have not written a program recently and have forgotten most of what they once knew about programming.

This book is not a reference book for True BASIC nor does it provide complete coverage of the language. I have kept it short on purpose and made it easy to read. It is not meant to be a textbook for professional programmers. The major purposes of the book are to introduce you to an easy-to-use computer language and to give you some idea of how computer programs are designed and indirectly, a deeper insight into how computer systems works.

The language used is True BASIC, a modern version of standard (ANS) BASIC. You must have access to the True BASIC language system, preferably by purchasing a copy of the Student Edition. In that case, you will have your own copy of the True BASIC Reference Manual, a valuable supplement to the textbook. Additional help is available from files on the enclosed floppy diskette.

Most engineering schools offer a programming course in FORTRAN or increasingly, in C++, designed for students who expect to become professional programmers. This textbook, of course, is not suitable for such a course.

In some engineering curricula, however, a course in BASIC is offered as an introductory first-year course to present the fundamental concepts of programming and prepare you for subsequent professional programming courses. In other curricula, the BASIC course may be all the formal training in computer programming you need, provided that you take subsequent courses requiring you to continue practicing and expanding your programming skills.

I hope you find this book, *Programming for Engineers... in True BASIC*, useful as you continue your engineering coursework and learn how to write computer programs.

If you have any comments, suggestions for enhancements or find any errors in the book, please do not hesitate to send me e-mail on the Internet at the address shown below.

Avery Catlin
ac@virginia.edu

Getting Started

Writing a computer program can be fun, it stimulates your mind. It's a little like doing crossword puzzles, an intellectual exercise. But writing programs can also produce real benefits. Most importantly, you learn more about your computer and how it works. You may save some of the programs that you write and use them in your daily work or activity. And every once in a while, you are able to help a friend by writing a computer program that solves a difficult real-life problem. So learning to write programs can both increase your knowledge of computers and help others.

Many of you may already know the information covered in Chapter 1. If so, just scan through the chapter to see if it contains any unfamiliar material.

1.1 FIRST STEPS

You must have access to a computer while reading this book. I am convinced that hands-on experience writing programs is necessary while learning any computer programming language. If you don't own a computer and have plans to buy one, read Appendix A. It gives advice on what to look for when purchasing a computer system and its application programs.

If you have never written a computer program, this book quickly provides enough information to get you started. In fact, you'll begin writing programs in Chapter 2. The BASIC language is used throughout because it is easy to understand and widely available. While there are several versions of BASIC, I have chosen to write this book for a version called True BASIC, developed by John Kemeny and Tom Kurtz, the original inventors of BASIC. You will learn and use True BASIC, the language in which the example programs are written. See Appendix A for information on how to purchase True BASIC.

Some of the terms used when discussing computer programming may be unfamiliar — they are defined in the following paragraphs. Computer people use lots of special words and abbreviations, you just have to get used to them.

Operating Your Computer

If possible, ask someone to help you the first time you sit down at your computer. It is almost impossible in a general book on programming to tell you which buttons to push or knobs to turn on your particular machine. There are too many variations from computer to computer. If you cannot find anyone to help you (or even if you can), read the manuals that came with your computer.

TIP: There should be a switch that turns on your computer, located on the front, side, or back of its case, or maybe on the keyboard. Your monitor may have a separate switch, as well as controls to adjust brightness and contrast.

You must learn how to turn on your computer, bring up the operating system (see a later definition) that you intend to use and start the True BASIC application. All simple tasks but confusing the first time — you may find it helpful to read Appendix B.

1.2 COMPUTER SYSTEMS

Here are definitions of the most important components in a computer system. If you are already familiar with computers, you can skim quickly over these items. The electrical and mechanical components are called *hardware* while the computer programs are called *software*. A complete computer system consists of both hardware and software.

There is a certain chicken-and-egg problem when defining computing terms. Sometimes, in order to describe a current term, you need to use a term that has not yet been defined. If you run into that situation in the following paragraphs, just glance ahead in the list of definitions and find the unknown term.

1.3 COMPUTER HARDWARE DEFINITIONS

The following items are part of the hardware in almost every computer system.

CPU

This is the central processing unit of the computer, it is the electronic brain that makes calculations based on program instructions. The way a CPU works is very simple, it is basically just a fast adding machine. This surprises many people who think that an electronic brain must be very sophisticated and smart.

The CPU has a special property, however, that makes it the wonderful tool it is — it can perform each addition in a millionth of a second or less. Thus a computer CPU is simple-minded but fast.

TIP: If you have a choice when buying your computer, choose the one with the fastest CPU. New application programs are becoming larger and do more work, requiring faster CPUs.

It's hard to visualize just how fast a millionth of a second really is. For example, assume the operator of a hand calculator can make one addition per second. This means the computer can do in one second what takes the calculator operator a million seconds.

That statement really doesn't give you a clear mental picture of the difference, but if you convert into units that are more familiar and remember that a human operator needs some time each day to eat and sleep, then the comparison becomes much more graphic. What the computer can do in ten minutes would take the calculator operator 80 years, more than a working lifetime. What a difference! So a special and valuable property of a computer CPU is its fast calculation speed.

The next time someone claims how smart a computer is, tell then its not smart, its dumb but awfully fast. It's their incredible speed that makes computers so powerful.

Memory

Memory consists of a grid of memory chips — small semiconductor devices — in which the computer stores information. When you turn off your computer, all information currently stored in memory disappears and is lost forever. Never forget that fact! A way to overcome this problem is discussed in the next section on disk drives.

Memory is sometimes called *RAM*, short for "random access memory." A *memory location* is the numeric address of a place in memory where the computer stores a particular item of information.

TIP: Most computers are sold with too little memory. Buy as much as you can afford. I recommend at least 16 Mb of RAM — see the following discussion for the meaning of the term "Mb."

Memory size is defined in terms of bits, the smallest unit of memory. The term *bit* means a binary digit or in terms of memory size, the minimum space needed to store a binary digit. You probably know that a *binary digit* can only have one of two values, 1 or 0. Sometimes these two values are described as true or false, other times as yes or no. All information stored in memory is stored as sequences of binary digits. When I say that a number is stored in 16 bits of memory, I also mean that enough space on a memory chip has been allocated to hold the 16 binary digits that represent that number.

A larger unit called the *byte* equals 8 bits. In the preceding example, a 16-bit number would require two bytes of memory storage space. A *kilobyte* (Kb) is one thousand bytes (more accurately, 1024 bytes). A *megabyte* (Mb) is 1024 kilobytes or about one million bytes. A *gigabyte* (Gb) is 1024 megabytes or about one billion bytes.

Disk Drive

This device, similar in operation to a CD disk player, stores information on magnetic disks. The information is stored in a relatively permanent form and can be quickly retrieved. Information stored on a disk is not lost when you turn off your computer system, whereas information stored in memory is lost. If a disk is physically damaged — chewed by your dog, for example — the information stored on it will probably be destroyed.

There are two general categories of disk drives, one for hard or *fixed disks* and one for *floppy disks* (also called *diskettes*). Fixed disks are usually not removable from the drive and have large storage capacities. A typical fixed disk can store hundreds of megabytes of data — the latest models store one or more gigabytes. Floppy disks are removable and are available in different sizes and capacities. They typically store about a megabyte of data but some new models can store over one hundred megabytes.

TIP: Many beginners are confused by the terms bit and byte. Remember, a byte is larger than a bit — one byte equals 8 bits.

Memory is much faster than a disk (maybe 100 to 1000 times faster), which means that it takes longer to write information on a disk than into memory. It also takes more time to read information from a disk. A fixed-disk drive is much faster when reading and writing than a floppy-disk drive.

Keyboard

The typewriterlike device with keys that you press to enter characters into the computer. When you press most keys, a character also appears on the monitor screen (see the following definition). A few keys are reserved for control purposes and pressing them does not produce a character.

Monitor

The televisionlike unit with a screen where characters are displayed. It is also called a *display unit*. Characters may be sent to the screen from the keyboard or from the computer itself. A special character on the screen called the *text cursor* is often a blinking underline or I-beam symbol and shows where the next character will appear when a key is pressed.

Mouse

This is a small device, about the size of your hand, that can be rolled across the desk top. When rolled, it moves an arrow cursor or a rectangular block cursor on the screen. This cursor is called the *mouse cursor*. A mouse has one to three buttons on its top that can be pressed to perform different functions. The device is a useful supplement to the keyboard, especially with a computer that displays graphics on its screen.

TIP: If your mouse has more than one button, you will use the left button most of the time. Some applications, however, also use the right button. If you use one of those applications that reacts to the right button, you should learn just what the right button does in your application.

The term *click* means to press and quickly release a mouse button when the mouse cursor is on top of or pointing to a desired object. This is normally the way you select a command from a menu on the screen. The term *double-click* means to press and release a mouse button twice in rapid succession. Double-clicking is often used to open a file or start an application.

If you run out of room on your desktop when rolling the mouse, don't panic. You don't need a bigger desk! Lift up the mouse and move it back through the air in the direction opposite to the direction it was rolling. Note that the cursor does not move when the mouse is lifted and moved. Put the mouse back down on the desktop and you can continue to roll it in the original direction, once again moving the cursor.

Printer

This is a device connected to your computer, directly or through a computer network, that prints characters or graphic images on paper as information is received from the computer.

1.4 COMPUTER SOFTWARE DEFINITIONS

In addition to hardware items like those defined in the preceding paragraphs, a computer must have software in order to operate and produce useful results. Here are a few more definitions:

Program

A program is a sequence of instructions to a computer, telling it how to accomplish a specific task. For example, the task might be to sort a list of names and print out the sorted list on a printer. The individual instructions are called *program statements*.

As a simple example, the program statement

```
PRINT "Betty Jean"
```

tells the computer to display the name `Betty Jean` on the screen.

Operating System

The operating system is a special program that controls the operation of a computer. It supervises computer operations, especially storage of information. An individual application, such as True BASIC, runs or executes under the supervision of the operating system. An important responsibility of the operating system is to maintain a directory of files on disk and supervise the writing and reading of these files.

TIP: Once again I'm using a word that has not been defined — files are defined in the following section on storage of information.

One of the most popular operating systems on IBM-compatible computers is *DOS*, an abbreviation for either MS-DOS (from Microsoft) or PC-DOS (from IBM). The letters DOS stand for "disk operating system." These computers are sometimes called DOS machines. A DOS machine usually displays a prompt on the monitor screen that may look as shown:

```
C:\>
```

When you see that prompt, you can enter a command that tells the computer what to do.

On the Apple Macintosh, the operating system is MacOS, sometimes further identified by a name like System 7.5. The Mac has a graphical screen, described in the following section.

GUI

A graphical user interface (GUI) is often available as part of an operating system and it makes a computer easier to use. A GUI is just what its name implies, a graphical screen display that the user can interact with, usually by moving and clicking a mouse. Instead of typing in a command, you use the mouse to select a command from a menu list that appears when the mouse button is clicked. Applications are often represented by little pictures called *icons*. You can start an application by double-clicking on its icon.

Fortunately, True BASIC can be used on many different computers with different interfaces. It has its own editor and editing screen on which you write program statements. Some users of IBM-compatible computers will choose to run True BASIC under DOS, others — and probably a growing number — will choose to run True BASIC under Windows (a popular GUI). The True BASIC language is essentially identical in both cases.

True BASIC is also a popular language on Apple Macintosh computers. In fact, it is one of the few versions of BASIC available for these fine machines. The MacOS operating system has a built-in GUI that has been refined steadily over the last decade.

One of the great advantages of True BASIC is that a program written for one kind of personal computer will usually run with zero or few changes on any other kind of personal computer.

Editor

An *editor* is a program that allows you to write text on the screen, modify that text, and then store it on a disk or print it on a printer. I am sure you are familiar with or have heard about a word processor — it is just a fancy editor. The True BASIC editor is normally used for writing programs but there is no reason it cannot also be used for writing anything you wish to write — like a note or a report.

Language System

Another kind of special program is a computer language system like True BASIC. It typically includes sections that translate and execute programs, carrying out the instructions in the program statements.

The first step in producing a program is to write a sequence of program statements in the BASIC language. You will be doing just that in the next chapter. This program you write is called the *source program*. As mentioned earlier, a text editor is part of the True BASIC language system and allows you to write and edit the source program.

The source program produced by the editor is read by the True BASIC system and translated into a sequence of binary instructions called the *object program*. A *binary instruction* — also called a machine language instruction — consists of one or more numbers in binary format that instruct the computer to do something. The process of telling the computer to follow these binary instructions is called *executing* the program and if the original program was written correctly, the desired results are obtained.

For example, the True BASIC statement

```
PRINT "A"
```

might translate into a machine language instruction something like the following sequence of binary numbers:

```
10110100 01000001 10110100 00000010 11001101 00100001
```

True BASIC statements in the source program make sense when read by human beings. Binary instructions in the object program make sense only to computers.

1.5 STORAGE OF INFORMATION

To understand how a computer operates, you must understand how it stores information. There are two important storage areas — disk files on both fixed and floppy disks and memory.

Files

A *file* is a collection of characters or other information, usually stored on a computer disk. Most computer languages store their program statements — their source program — in a disk file. A unique name identifies each file and a directory of all files is maintained on disk by the disk operating system.

Any collection of text characters, such as a list of addresses or a letter to a friend, may be stored in a file. A file that is a collection of readable characters is called a *text file* and can be displayed on the screen and read. True BASIC source programs are stored on disk as text files.

Another type of file contains only binary numbers and is called a *binary file*. This kind of file cannot be displayed on the screen, in readable format, by a text editor. Most computer applications (including the True BASIC language system files) are binary files.

Why the two kinds of files? Most files that are executed — applications like word processors or language systems — must be stored as binary files. They contain binary numbers representing machine language instructions and thus can be understood by the computer. On the other hand, source program statements and lists of information are most convenient to handle if kept in a format that can be easily read and modified by the user. These items are often stored as text files.

Another type of file in True BASIC is the record file, not discussed in this book. A record file is used to hold information that must be accessed at random, something you cannot do in a text file. It cannot be displayed on the screen with a simple editor.

DOS File Names

Every file stored on disk is identified by a *file name*. In DOS, this file name can be up to eight characters long and may be followed by an optional period and a three-character extension. Consult your DOS manual for details, especially for information on which characters are not allowed in file names.

TIP: The space character can never be used in a DOS file name.

An extension is often used to denote the kind of file. For example, the extension `TRU` identifies a True BASIC source program file, while the extension `DOC` identifies a Microsoft Word document file. You can sometimes make up your own rules on the meaning of extensions but it is better to follow recommendations from the software manufacturer.

Watch out for one peculiarity of the True BASIC editor. If you save a file with the name `SAMPLE02`, it will automatically be given the extension `TRU` and stored under the file name `SAMPLE02.TRU`. If you really want the file named without an extension, save it as `SAMPLE02.` (note the trailing period) and it will be stored as `SAMPLE02` with no extension. Kind of confusing, isn't it?

Mac File Names

The Apple Macintosh computer has fewer restrictions on file names. Spaces are allowed in file names and there is no equivalent of the DOS file name extension. File names can be up to 63 characters long and may contain any character except a colon. Mac file names can be much more descriptive than DOS file names.

DOS Path Names

Files are stored on disk in groups called *directories*. Each disk has a primary directory called the *root directory* and within that directory, there may be other named directories. Directories can be nested to any depth.

Every file is also identified by a unique name called its *path name*. The path name consists of the disk drive letter, a sequence of directory names showing just where the file is stored in the disk's hierarchical directory structure, and the file name. A backslash, representing the root directory, appears immediately following the disk drive letter and colon. Other backslashes in the path name serve to separate individual directory names.

TIP: Neither the DOS nor the Mac operating systems differentiate between lowercase and uppercase letters in file and path names.

Two files can have the same file name but each must have a unique path name. Once again, read your DOS manual to learn how to construct a path name. Here are two examples of DOS path names:

```
A:\SCORES.TXT
```

A text file named SCORES.TXT is stored in the root directory of the disk in drive A, usually a floppy disk drive.

```
C:\HWORK\WEEK5\MY_TEST.TRU
```

True BASIC program MY_TEST.TRU is stored in directory WEEK5 which is in the directory HWORK which in turn is in the root directory of disk C. Note use of the underline character to separate words in the file name.

Mac Path Names

The Apple Macintosh also has a unique path name for every file. The Mac file directory is usually called a *file folder*. Folders can be nested, one within another, in the same manner as directories. The Mac path name differs from the DOS path name by starting with a disk name rather than a disk drive letter, by having folder names instead of directory names, and by using a colon as a separator instead of a backslash. Names of disks, folders, and files cannot contain colons because the colon is reserved for use as a separator.

Path names are seldom used when manipulating files because the Mac operating environment is largely graphical. Files are copied, deleted, or otherwise edited by moving their icon with the mouse. In True BASIC programs, however, Mac path names are commonly used to identify files used in the program. A typical Mac path name might be:

```
Boot Disk:Programs:test data
```

This path name refers to a file named "test data" in a folder named "Programs" on the disk named "Boot Disk." Mac path names, like DOS path names, are not sensitive to case — either lowercase or uppercase characters can be used.

Memory Used for Storage

Memory has already been defined but its volatile nature has not been emphasized. When your computer is turned off, or if there is the slightest interruption or flicker of your electrical power supply, all information stored in memory can be lost. If you have not saved your work for the past hour or so, the loss is devastating!

That is the reason for recommending that you save your work frequently when you are writing a program — or for that matter, when you are creating any new text or graphic images with a computer. The process of saving identifies a specific block of memory where you have been working, makes a copy of the contents of that block, and stores the copy in a disk file. Here it is relatively safe — at least from power interruptions. See your True BASIC manual for details.

IMPORTANT TIP: You ***must*** develop the habit of saving your program on disk, at least once every 15 minutes or so.

Storing Numbers and Characters

As discussed in preceding paragraphs, every item of information in a computer is stored in memory as a sequence of binary digits. A decimal number is converted to binary format and stored, you don't need to be concerned at this time about how it is done. The digital computer is a numeric machine at heart and the only kind of information it knows how to manipulate and store is numeric information.

Because computer memory can store only numbers, all characters — including the digit characters 0, 1, 2, ... , 9 — must be encoded using a coding scheme. The most common coding scheme is the ASCII scheme which assigns a number between 0 and 256 to each of the alphabetic, digital, punctuation, and other commonly used characters. For example, the ASCII value of the letter A is 65, the ASCII value of the digit 9 is 57, the ASCII value of a period is 46. This ASCII value is stored in memory, not the character itself. When storing any character, its ASCII value must be converted from decimal format to binary format before storage. Remember — digital computers store only binary-formatted numbers in memory, nothing else.

Many people have difficulty understanding this difference between numbers and characters. I have often heard the comment, "If a 9 is stored in the computer, why can't I just retrieve it and add 1 to get 10?" If 9 is stored as a number, you can indeed use the addition operation to add 1 to it and get 10.

However, if 9 is stored in memory as a character (the digit character 9), it is stored as its ASCII value which is 57. If you could add 1 to the stored value (which you can't actually do with a simple addition operation), you would get an ASCII value of 58 which is the code for the colon character. As you can see, addition makes no sense in this case.

Remember that this discussion applies to storing values in memory, not to storing values on disk. There are significant differences. I will explain disk storage in some detail in Chapter 5.

WHAT YOU HAVE LEARNED

This section appears at the end of each chapter and serves as your check sheet. If you look at the table in Fig. 1.1 and say to yourself, "Gosh, I don't remember anything about GUI," then you should go back to page 6 and glance over the material on GUI again. Technical information can be dull and all of us have blind spots when reading. The table helps identify any material you may have missed in the first reading.

In most cases, lack of understanding of technical details doesn't affect your ability to write programs. As you read through the book, some ideas that seem difficult at first will become clear. Don't give up — keep reading! Keep your computer handy and turned on. I want you to use your computer at every opportunity as you read through the rest of the book.

Topic	Page
Computer hardware definitions	2
The high speed of computer calculations	3
The meaning of bits and bytes	3
How to use a mouse	5
Computer software definitions	5
The meaning of GUI	6
Source programs and binary instructions	8
File and path names	8
The importance of saving a program frequently	11
Storing numbers and characters	11

Figure 1.1—*What you have learned in Chapter 1.*

Terms Defined in Chapter 1

application program computer program that performs a specific task; see **editor**

ASCII coding scheme used to represent characters in a digital computer

binary file file of binary instructions

binary instruction sequence of binary numbers that tells the computer to do something

bit binary digit, has value of 0 or 1

byte unit of eight bits

click press left mouse button when mouse cursor is on selected object

compiler translates a source program into an object program

CPU central processing unit (an electronic chip) of a computer

directory named space on disk where files can be stored, DOS term

disk rotating magnetic platter where files are stored

display unit televisionlike screen that displays text and graphics

double-click click mouse twice in rapid succession

editor computer program for creating and modifying files

file named sequence of text characters or binary numbers, usually stored on disk

file folder named space on disk where files can be stored, MacOS term

file name name associated with a specific file

fixed disk disk, usually non-removable, with a large storage capacity

floppy diskette removable disk with limited storage capacity

gigabyte 1024 megabytes or about one billion bytes

GUI graphical user interface that displays graphics on the monitor screen

hardware mechanical and electrical components of a computer system

icon little picture on a GUI that represents a program

Internet: óa world-wide computer network using telephone links between computers

keyboard typerwriterlike device for entering characters into the computer

kilobyte: 1024 bytes

machine language instruction see binary instruction

MacOS operating system for Apple Macintosh computers

megabyte 1024 kilobytes or about one million bytes

memory electronic chips that store information in a computer

memory address location of a specific memory byte, expressed as a number

monitor see display unit

mouse cursor block or arrow cursor that moves when mouse is moved

MS-DOS Microsoft disk operating system for IBM PC-compatible computers

object program program of binary instructions

operating system software that supervises computer operations and manages files

path name file name plus directory name(s) specifying the location of a file

PC-DOS IBM disk operating system for IBM PC computers

printer device to print computer output on paper

program statement language statement that when compiled, tells computer to do something

RAM random access memory, see memory

root directory primary disk directory from which all others branch

software operating system and application programs of a computer system

source program program of language (True BASIC) statements

text cursor underline or I-beam cursor showing insertion point of next character

text file file of ASCII text characters

True BASIC advanced BASIC language, complies with the ANSI standard for BASIC

Windows Microsoft GUI usually built on MS-DOS

Output, Input and Variables

In this chapter, you learn how to read input from the keyboard and write output on the screen. At last you can talk with the computer! In order to write input statements, you must also learn about variables — just memory locations with names where information is stored.

2.1 YOUR FIRST PROGRAM

TIP: Before starting any new application, always learn how to stop it. You can stop True BASIC by dragging down the File menu with the mouse and selecting the Quit command. If you don't know about dragging, type in the `BYE` command after an Ok. prompt.

I promised that you would write a program in Chapter 2, so here goes! Before you start, however, read Appendix B. This appendix discusses how to start the True BASIC language system on different computers and under different operating systems. Unless stated otherwise, this chapter is written primarily for an IBM PC-compatible computer using the MS-DOS operating system.

In DOS versions of True BASIC prior to Version 5, the screen is divided into two parts. The upper part is called the *source* window, it is here that programs are written and edited. The lower part is called the *command* window and the last line displayed is an Ok. prompt. You can enter any True BASIC command following this prompt. You can move to either window by clicking the mouse button when the block mouse cursor is in the desired window. Under DOS, the F1 function key moves the cursor to the source window; the F2 key, to the command window — try it yourself and see what happens.

In Version 5 or if you are using MacOS on a Macintosh, only the editing window is displayed initially. You write your program in that window.

Move the cursor to the source window — often called the *editing* window — and write the following program lines on the screen, exactly as shown on the next page:

```
REM Example Program 2-1

PRINT "Good morning!"
END
```

Press the Return or Enter key at the end of each line. Press the Return key only, without a statement, to create a blank line. As you may have guessed, this program displays the following phrase in the command or output window:

```
Good morning!
```

Be sure to write and execute this program yourself. In fact, as you read through the book, you should write and execute every example program.

If you are using a Mac, your keyboard may have both an Enter key and a Return key. Press the Return key at the end of each program line, not the Enter key.

If you are using Version 5 of True BASIC with Windows, look in your True BASIC manual and learn how to make your computer pause so you can read program output before it is erased from the screen. You will see that you must add a `GET KEY X` statement to your program, just before the `END` statement.

No Line Numbers

If you have used other versions of BASIC, you may notice the absence of line numbers. Early versions of BASIC relied heavily on line numbers, modern versions usually omit them. They are seldom needed in today's programs.

Writing a Program

So that is all there is to writing a program — it looks pretty simple, doesn't it? Each True BASIC statement must be on a separate program line. As you write, you are using a text editor and can make corrections as needed. Use the mouse to move the mouse cursor — the one that moves when the mouse is moved — to any place in the text, then click at that point to position the blinking text cursor there. Characters are inserted to the left of the blinking cursor.

You can also move the text cursor directly with the four arrow keys on your keyboard. You erase characters using the Delete or Backspace keys (if your keyboard has both keys, try them both and see how they differ). You insert characters by moving the text cursor to the insertion point and then typing in the desired characters.

Executing a Program

When you have finished writing your program, select the `Run` command from the Run menu to execute it. To drag down a menu, move the mouse cursor over the menu title, hold down the mouse button while moving the cursor to the desired command name, and release the button. The command you selected (`Run`) is executed and program output is displayed in the command or output window. You can also execute the current program — the program displayed in the source window — by typing the command `Run` after the Ok. prompt. Output appears in the source window.

Under Windows in the latest versions of True BASIC, the menu will appear as soon as you click on the Run menu title — you don't have to drag it down — and when it does appear, you can click on the `Run` command. Output appears in a separate window, the output window.

How This Program Works

Let's examine each of the four lines in the example program in detail. The first program line or statement is a remark, identified by the letters `REM`. A remark is just a note written by and for the benefit of the programmer. It is ignored by the computer when the program is run and thus is not executed.

The second line is a blank line. You can put as many blank lines as you want into a program, their purpose is to make the program more readable. Blank lines are also ignored by the computer.

The third line is a `PRINT` statement that displays on screen the characters enclosed within quotation marks. This statement is executed by the computer.

An `END` statement must be the last line in every True BASIC program and only one `END` statement is allowed in a program. This `END` statement announces the end of the program and in Version 5 under Windows, closes the output window. In MacOS, pressing any key closes the output window.

Version 5 is designed to run under a GUI — specifically Windows and MacOS — and in that environment, programs expect the user to take some action to exit a program. That is the only purpose of the `GET KEY X` statement in a Windows program. It makes the computer pause until the user presses a key — any key — and then tells the computer to execute the next statement, in this case the `END` statement. If a `GET KEY X` statement is not included, there is no pause, the output window is closed as soon as the `END` statement is executed, and you only have a second or so to look at the results. Here is a slightly different program for Version 5 under Windows:

```
REM Example Program 2-1
REM Modified for Version 5.

PRINT "Good morning!"
GET KEY X
END
```

By the way, the `X` in the `GET KEY X` statement is called a *dummy variable* — the only purpose of the statement is to make program execution pause until a key is pressed.

Saving a Program

Let's concentrate for a moment on the File menu. When you drag down this menu, you see several useful and important commands.

The `Save` command saves your current program on disk. If the program has not been named — if its name is Untitled — you are asked to specify a file name. You don't need to add an extension to your DOS file name, the True BASIC system automatically adds the extension `TRU`. Remember that in MacOS file name extensions are not commonly used.

The `Save As` command allows you to save a named file under a new name and in a new location. Otherwise, it is the same as the `Save` command.

The `New` command, in DOS versions of True BASIC, clears the editing window so you can write a new program. If you have not saved your current file, you are prompted to do so. In Windows (with Version 5) and MacOS, you must first use the `Clear` command and then follow it with the `New` command.

I know that the variation in commands for different versions of True BASIC and for different operating systems is confusing. Don't worry too much about it, you will quickly learn the proper commands for your own version of True BASIC and your own operating system. Read the user's manual for help.

A Useful Program

That first program was short and easy to write but not very useful. Here is another program that is almost as short but may be more useful. It displays the current time on the screen. Exclamation marks are used here instead of `REM`s — they both serve the same purpose, identifying remark or comment statements. A remark starting with an exclamation mark can also appear after any statement on the same line as the statement. `Time$` is the name of a True BASIC function, a program element that calculates a value — in this case, the current time.

```
! Example Program 2-2
! Display the current time.

PRINT Time$   ! Time$ is a True BASIC function
END
```

The program reads the computer's clock which keeps track of the current time. It displays the following output in the usual 24-hour format:

```
18:12:22
```

2.2 LEARNING BY DOING

Learning is an active process. In this section, I discuss some ways to help you learn the True BASIC system and language.

Learn from the Help Command

The Help command provides help on any of the True BASIC commands. The best way to access this help from DOS is by typing the following command in the command window. The words you type are in italics for emphasis:

```
Ok. HELP Topics
```

A list of available topics is displayed on the screen. Each topic is one of the True BASIC commands. Find the command that you want help on and then press the Return key to clear the screen and display the Ok. prompt again.

Let's assume you want help on the Hello command. Type the command

```
Ok. HELP Hello
```

and you can read information about using the HELLO command. Another way to get help is to press the F10 key and then enter the topic, in this case Hello. The same information screen is displayed.

If using MacOS, pull down the Help menu with your mouse and select Help... or Help Topics. Once again, help is limited to commands.

The Help command in Version 5 is much more useful. It is essentially the hyperlinked text of the complete True BASIC reference manual. It also contains source code segments — useful for showing how statements work — and these segments can be loaded into the program that you are writing.

Supplementary Help Files

While writing this book, prior to the release of the newest versions of True BASIC, I often found that I needed to look up the exact syntax of a True BASIC statement or refresh my memory on the purpose of a specific function. I decided to create three supplementary help files and place them in the True BASIC directory. Here they can be accessed using the Old or Open command in the File menu and the desired information can be found using the Find command in the Edit menu.

The first file, named STATMENT.TRU, contains syntax information on all True BASIC statements in the current Student Edition. The spelling of the file name is deliberate — remember the eight-letter limit on DOS file names.

The second file, named FUNCTION.TRU, contains similar information on all built-in functions in the Student Edition. I discuss many of these functions in Chapter 6.

The third file, named `TERMS.TRU`, contains definitions of new computer terminology introduced in this book (also see pages __ and __). These three files should be stored in the same directory as True BASIC.

Let's suppose you want to find out more about the function `Time$`. Access the proper file by entering the following command:

```
Ok. OLD FUNCTION
```

With the `FUNCTION.TRU` file displayed in the source window, use the `Find` command to find the function name `Time$`. Information on the use and syntax of that function is displayed. I hope you find these files as useful as I have.

Learn by Experimenting

Don't hesitate to learn by experimenting, writing short programs to test unfamiliar statements and syntax. As you write and execute each of the example programs, try changing some of the lines (of course, using proper syntax as shown in the user's manual) and see what happens. I find that such experimentation is often a great help when learning a new computer language.

Try using the `PRINT` statement in different ways, displaying both numbers and groups of characters enclosed in quotation marks — these character groups are called *strings*. Quotation marks are only required around strings, not numbers. Try statements like the following that contain one or more items and see what they displays:

```
PRINT "The unit requires"; 120; "volts"
PRINT "and draws 15 amperes."
```

Note that True BASIC automatically adds a space before and after a number but displays without change the characters enclosed in quotation marks.

Experiment further and try replacing semicolon separators with commas in the first statement. What happens? Notice that the comma separator displays items in widely separated columns, 16 spaces apart by default. Try adding a trailing semicolon to the first statement — that is, add a semicolon as the last character. What happens now? You have to add a space before the word "`and`" in the second statement to make the output look correct, don't you? Remember that! You can learn a lot from this kind of experimentation.

I hope you experimented on your own computer before reading the answer about the effect of a trailing semicolon — it suppresses the carriage return and line feed that normally occur at the end of a `PRINT` statement.

2.3 VARIABLES AND THEIR USE

Now that you are over the hurdle of writing and executing your first program, I introduce the concept of a *variable* in a computer program — the name of a memory location where information is stored. The name of a variable can be up to 31 characters long. Think of it as a named box, kind of like an old shoebox you might keep in a closet, in which numbers or character strings can be stored. Variables are used in almost every True BASIC program.

Numbers and Strings

You already know about two types of *data* — numbers and strings — from the preceding discussions. A number is a numeric value expressed as a sequence of digits, possibly with a decimal point and a plus or minus sign. A string is a sequence of any characters, usually enclosed in quotation marks. You may remember that you learned about the storage of these two types in Chapter 1. If you have forgotten, go back and read the discussion on page 10.

TIP: Look in Appendix D for information on displaying numeric values, especially in exponential or scientific notation.

One type of variable — thinking of a variable as a storage box — can contain only a number, it's called a *numeric variable* and its initial contents are the number zero. Another type of box can contain only a string, it's called a *string variable* and its initial contents are a null string. A *null string* means a string containing no characters; in other words, the string is empty. A string variable name always has a single dollar sign ($) as its last character to distinguish it from a numeric variable name. All variable names are limited to 31 characters.

Select your variable names with care, they should be descriptive and thus make your program easier to read. Avoid the temptation to use single-letter names except possibly for an index or for numeric variables in equations. For example, `Radius` and `FirstName$` are both good, descriptive variable names.

One other word of warning: A variable name cannot be a True BASIC reserved word. A list of reserved words appears in Appendix C. If you try to use a reserved word as a variable name, you create an error and your program will not run.

Program Style

Programs are easier to read, and thus to understand, if you follow a recommended style when writing them. I use all uppercase letters for True BASIC keywords and the initial word in every statement. I start the names of functions (and other procedures) and variables with an uppercase letter. Names of variables and functions can contain letters, digits, underline characters, and a single, final dollar sign.

The first character in a name must be a letter. If a name is created from two or more English words, I capitalize each word in the name. Some programmers prefer to write variable names in lowercase characters without the first letter capitalized. Make your own choice but be consistent.

Assigning a Numeric Value

The information stored in a variable is called its *value*. An *assignment statement* assigns a value to a variable.

If a numeric variable is named `Count`, the statement

```
LET Count = 245
```

assigns the value 245 to the variable `Count`. In other words, the number 245 is stored in the memory location identified by the name `Count`. If a value already exists in a memory location when a new value is assigned, the existing value is overwritten and effectively erased.

The Assignment Operator

The equal sign (=) is the assignment operator. Assignment means nothing more than placing a value in the box — or memory location — corresponding to the variable name. The type of value and variable must match; that is, a numeric value can only be assigned to a numeric variable, a string value to a string variable.

Beginning programmers sometimes mistake the assignment statement for an equality statement, equating the quantities on either side of the equal sign to each other. As you will see later, when computer decision making is introduced, an equal sign symbol can also be used as an equality operator. The two statements, however, are quite different. The program content normally shows clearly which is which, especially if you use the keyword `LET` as the first word in an assignment statement.

Consider the following program statement:

```
LET Count = Count + 1
```

It is obvious that this statement is not an equality. What it means is that the old value of `Count` is taken out of the variable box, the number 1 is added to the old value, and the new, modified value of `Count` is then placed back in the box. This process is called "incrementing the value of `Count` by one" and it is a common process in many programs.

Some versions of BASIC allow assignment statements without the keyword `LET`. You can write statements in that style if you place the statement

```
OPTION NOLET
```

near the beginning of your program. The preceding assignment statement is then written:

```
Count = Count + 1
```

I recommend, however, that you continue to write assignment statements using LET. I think its use makes True BASIC programs a little easier to read. Its omission can also produce erratic error messages.

Simple Arithmetic with Numeric Variables

There are five common arithmetic operators, as follows:

+	addition
-	subtraction
*	multiplication
/	division
^	exponentiation (the caret symbol)

You are undoubtedly familiar with the first four operations although the operator for multiplication (an asterisk) may be strange to you. Exponentiation is just a fancy word for raising a number to a power, thus 4 squared or 4^2 is written as 4^2 in a True BASIC expression.

You may wonder whether square roots can be calculated as well as squares? The answer is yes, in two different ways. To calculate the square root of 4, you can raise 4 to the 1/2 power using the expression 4^(0.5). There is also a square root function. The square root of 4 is written as `Sqr(4)` in a True BASIC expression and produces a value of 2. I discuss this and other functions in Chapter 7.

A *numeric expression* is defined as two or more numeric values, numeric variables, or numeric functions joined together with arithmetic operators. A numeric function is one that produces a numeric result, like `Sqr(4)`. Here is an example of a numeric expression:

```
X + 12 - Sqr(4)
```

where the variable X has already been assigned a value.

At this point, I encourage you once again to experiment yourself, writing simple BASIC programs that perform numeric calculations.

Here is an example program that calculates the volume of a cylindrical tank, 7 feet in overall length and 3 feet in diameter, with flat ends.

```
! Example Program 2-3
! Calculate the volume of a cylindrical tank.

LET Diameter = 3
LET Radius = Diameter/2
```

```
LET Length = 7
LET Volume = (3.1416 * (Radius^2)) * Length
PRINT "Volume is"; Volume; "cubic feet"
END
```

The following output is produced:

```
Volume is 49.4802 cubic feet
```

If someone gave you that answer, you might wonder, "Why all the digits? Who are they trying to impress?" As an engineering student, you probably recognize that the precision implied by the answer (four digits after the decimal point) is not justified by the precision of Radius and Length. You might be happier with an answer like 49 cubic feet or possibly, 49.5 cubic feet.

Formatting Output from Variables

It is easy to change the preceding program so it displays an integer (whole number) answer or an answer with a specified number of digits after the decimal point. Use the rounding function — `Round(X, N)` — that *returns* (calculates) the number `X` rounded to `N` digits after the decimal point. In your program, write the `PRINT` statement as follows:

```
PRINT "Volume is"; Round(Volume, 1); "cubic feet"
```

and the following output is produced:

```
Volume is 49.5 cubic feet
```

That looks a lot better, doesn't it?

Value of Pi

There is one more change that you might make to improve your program. The constant pi, 3.1416..., is used so often that a special function named `Pi` has been created in True BASIC, giving the value correct to at least 10 decimal places. You might as well use that value in your program instead of using a numeric constant.

Enough changes have now been discussed that an improved version of the program, designated Example Program 2-4, can be written:

```
! Example Program 2-4
! Calculate the volume of a cylindrical tank.

LET Diameter = 3
LET Radius = Diameter/2
LET Length = 7
LET Volume = (Pi * (Radius^2)) * Length
PRINT "Volume is"; Round(Volume, 1); "cubic feet"
END
```

This revised program produces the desired output:

```
Volume is 49.5 cubic feet
```

Challenge Program 2-1

From time to time, I will insert a challenge problem in the text. These problems challenge you to write a program that solves a real problem. Program solutions are listed in a separate Challenge Problem Solutions manual but don't look at them now — try to solve the problem yourself. The only way to learn how to solve problems is to practice.

Having calculated the volume of a cylindrical tank with flat ends in Example Program 2-4, now calculate the volume of a cylindrical tank with hemispherical ends. The diameter and overall length of the tank remain the same. Look up the formula for the volume of a sphere in a dictionary or handbook. Should your calculated volume be less than or more than 49.5 cubic feet? Why might a designer specify a tank with hemispherical ends?

Assigning and Concatenating Strings

Let's talk a little more about assigning a string value to a variable. In the first place, the variable must be a string variable with a dollar sign ($) as the last character in its name. In the second place, a string value or constant must be enclosed in quotation marks. Thus the statement

```
LET ItemName$ = "portable multimeter"
```

assigns a string value to the string variable `ItemName$`. Of course, when the value of `ItemName$` is displayed on the screen, the quotation marks don't show.

In contrast to numbers, the only operation available for strings — equivalent to the arithmetic operations with numbers — is *concatenation*, defined as the joining together of two or more string values. The concatenation operator is the ampersand (&). Look at the following example:

```
! Example Program 2-5
! Join three strings together
! and display the result.

LET Color$ = "red"
LET Control$ = "switch"
LET Name$ = Color$ & " " & Control$
PRINT Name$
END
```

A one-character string, consisting of a single blank, is placed between the strings `Color$` and `Control$` to form the string `Name$`. The resulting full name is displayed:

```
red switch
```

TIP: Concatenation creates a new string that can then be printed. Displaying several strings with a single `PRINT` statement does not create a new string.

A string expression is defined as a string function (discussed in Chapter 6) or the concatenation —joining together — of two or more string values, string variables, or string functions. An example of a string expression is the one used in the preceding program:

```
Color$ & " " & Control$
```

2.4 READING FROM THE KEYBOARD

Now that you have learned about variables, let's discuss the process of entering information from the keyboard.

The INPUT Statement

Characters typed on the keyboard are assigned to a variable by the `INPUT` statement. Here is an example:

```
INPUT Result$
```

This statement displays a question mark and a space, and then waits for the user to type in information. If the user does nothing, nothing happens! In normal circumstances, the user types in a result like *Test failed at 120 psi* and then presses the Return key. The program responds by assigning the 22 characters — Test failed at 120 psi — to the string variable Result$.

TIP: There are 22 characters, not 18, because the 4 spaces count as characters.

The INPUT Prompt

A plain `INPUT` statement is not very useful because it gives the user no idea what input is desired. A better version of the `INPUT` statement adds a prompt:

```
INPUT prompt "Test result? ": Result$
```

The prompt string is a phrase enclosed in quotation marks, placed directly after the phrase "`INPUT prompt`" and separated from the variable by a colon. The prompt characters are displayed before the user enters input. A question mark and trailing space are not displayed automatically, they must be part of the prompt string.

If a user enters the result in the preceding paragraph, the screen dialog would look as follows:

```
Test result? Test failed at 120 psi
```

The first phrase, ending with a question mark and a space, is produced by the computer program, while the result itself is typed in by the user.

TIP: Let me make it clear that you type ordinary letters, not italic letters, in response to an `INPUT` statement. I use italic face in the book just to show which characters are typed by the user.

More Example Programs

Here is a complete computer program containing both input and output:

```
! Example Program 2-6
! Demonstrate both input and output.

INPUT prompt "Item name? : ": ItemName$
PRINT "The item name is "; ItemName$
END
```

It displays the following display on the screen when it is executed:

```
Enter the item name: multimeter
The item name is multimeter
```

Another example program demonstrates input and output of numeric quantities:

```
! Example Program 2-7
! Show input and output of numeric quantities.

PRINT "An integer is a whole number."
PRINT
INPUT prompt "Enter a positive integer: ": NumValue
LET NumValue = NumValue + 1
PRINT "The next positive integer is"; NumValue
END
```

It shows the following screen display:

```
An integer is a whole number.

Enter a positive integer: 27
The next positive integer is 28
```

Did you notice that I added a variation of the `PRINT` statement you haven't used before? The word `PRINT` on a line by itself just displays a blank line — it prints nothing. In an earlier section, I showed a statement to increment the value of a numeric variable and a statement of that kind — incrementing the value of `NumValue` — is part of this program.

Look carefully at one difference in the syntax of the `INPUT` statement and the last `PRINT` statement. A space is placed just before the closing quotation mark of the `INPUT` statement prompt, but not before the closing quotation mark of the last

PRINT statement. You should understand and be able to explain this difference; if not, read the following answer.

All these syntax details can be confusing and may seem like nit-picking but they are important. You must know about them if you want to achieve a specific program output. In fact, your program may not run if the syntax is wrong. See the help files or your manual for details and continue to experiment yourself.

ANSWER: A space in the last character position of an INPUT prompt creates a space before the first character typed. If it is left out, the line is less readable. In a PRINT statement, a space usually is not needed as the last character before or as the first character after a numeric value. Numeric values are automatically displayed with both a leading and a trailing space unless the numeric value is negative, in which case the leading space is replaced by a minus sign.

Challenge Problem 2-2

Write a program that converts a temperature in degrees Celsius to the equivalent temperature in degrees Fahrenheit. Don't go running for your physics book to look up the formulas, work them out yourself. You should know that the boiling point of water is 100 degrees C and 212 degrees F. The freezing point is 0 degrees C and 32 degrees F. That range between freezing and boiling is 100 degrees C and 180 degrees F, a ratio of 5 to 9.

Furthermore, the range starts at 0 for Celsius temperatures and at 32 for Fahrenheit temperatures. The difference in the start of the range, 32, must be added to get a correct Fahrenheit temperature after you apply the ratio to the Celsius temperature.

That's all the information you need — now develop your own formulas, test them, write a conversion program in True BASIC, and test it to be certain it gives accurate results. If you want a little more practice, write a similar program that converts a Fahrenheit temperature to Celsius.

WHAT YOU HAVE LEARNED

This has been a long chapter, I discussed topics in more detail than I will in many future chapters. Be sure to become familiar with the help files, I believe you will find them useful. And be sure to supplement information in the book by experimenting with True BASIC statements and programs on your own computer.

Topic	Page
How to write your first program	15
Line numbers not needed in True BASIC	16
How this program works	17
Using the supplementary help files	19
Learning by experimenting	20
Separators in PRINT statements	20
Numbers and strings	21
Assignment of values to variables	22
Simple arithmetic operators	23
Controlling the format of screen displays	24
Concatenating strings	25
Using the INPUT statement	26

Figure 2.1*—What you have learned in Chapter 2.*

Terms Defined in Chapter 2

arithmetic operator add (+), subtract (-), multiply (*), divide (/), or exponentiation (^)

assignment operator the equal sign (=)

assignment statement LET keyword

Bye command: exit the True BASIC system

Clear command erase the current program, from File menu

command window lower window where commands are entered

concatenation join two strings together, operator is the ampersand (&)

current program program presently running or in the editing window

drag down put cursor on menu title, hold mouse button down, and pull down the menu

editing window upper window where programs are edited

equality operator the equal sign (=)

Find command find a sequence of characters, from Edit menu or command line

FUNCTION.TRU file help file containing a list of all built-in functions

line number unique number identifying a program statement

New command create a new program, from File menu

null string an empty string, contains no characters

number: numeric value, a real number

numeric expression: formula or function that yields a numeric value

numeric variable named memory location where a number can be stored

Old command: open an existing program, from command line

Open command: open an existing program, from File menu

output window window where program results are displayed, Version 5

program output: results produced when a program is executed or run

Quit command exit the True BASIC system

remark statement non-executable program statement that makes a comment

Run command execute the current program, from Run menu or command line

Save As command save the current program with a new name, from File menu

Save command save the current program, from File menu or command line

source window window where the source program is displayed, Version 5

STATMENT.TRU file help file containing a list of all program statements

string string value, a sequence of one or more ASCII characters

string expression formula or function that yields a string value

string variable named memory location where a string can be stored

TERMS.TRU file help file for computer terms and their definitions

variable named memory location where information can be stored

variable value numeric, string, or array value stored in a named memory location

CHAPTER

3

Arrays and Simple Loops

Sometimes a simple variable does not meet your needs. In this chapter, you learn about a new type of variable, the *array* variable, that can store sets of numeric or string values. In order to store information in arrays, you need a program structure that repeats one or more instructions a number of times. That structure is called a *loop* and you learn how to write a simple loop.

3.1 ANOTHER VARIABLE TYPE: THE ARRAY

As an example of the use of an array variable, suppose you are collecting information on the physical condition of highway bridges in a rural county. This county contains 23 bridges. There are 5 teams of engineers inspecting bridges and at every bridge, they measure the natural frequency of that bridge. Several teams are used to measure the natural frequency of each bridge at different times because the frequency value may be affected by external conditions like temperature and by characteristics of the measuring equipment. Natural frequency is one physical property, along with several others, that determines how a bridge will react and how safe it will be when subjected to an external force such as a wind storm or an earthquake. A table is needed to record all the information — 115 individual frequency measurements. These natural frequencies are normally in the range of 2 to 9 *hertz*.

TIP: The unit hertz is the international unit for frequency, equal to one cycle per second. For example, the AC power in your house has a frequency of 60 hertz.

Storing a Table of Information

One method of handling this information is to store it in a spreadsheet, a form often used by accountants. You could use 23 rows for the individual bridges and 5 columns, one for each inspection team. Each bridge would be identified by a row label; that is, the frequency values for bridge 1 would be kept in a row labeled Bridge 1, those for bridge 5 in row Bridge 5, and so forth. Each team's measurements would be identified by a column label; that is, all the measurements made by team 1 would be in a column labeled Team 1, those by team 3 in column Team

3, and so forth. That seems a logical way to store the data. Fig. 3.1 shows the top left corner of such a spreadsheet.

	Team 1	Team 2	Team 3
Bridge 1	3.7	3.9	3.8
Bridge 2	5.2	5.5	5.7

Figure 3.1 *Top left corner of a spreadsheet*

Let's imagine, however, that you want to store this information in a True BASIC program, not in a spreadsheet. You could use 115 (23 times 5) simple numeric variables to store the natural bridge frequencies but that means you would need 115 different assignment statements in your program just to assign and store this information.

Creating a Two-Dimensional Numeric Array Variable

An array or indexed variable is needed to store efficiently this type of information. An *indexed variable* is a special kind of variable identified by one or more indices. Your particular array needs two indices, one to identify the bridge and the other to identify the team. An array with two indices is the variable equivalent of a spreadsheet.

An *index* is just a counter. In this case there are two counters, one keeping track of the individual bridges and the other, the individual inspection teams. Indices can have only integer (whole number) values.

Let's see how you can specify a new type of variable, an *array variable*, to hold all this information. First, the new variable needs a name. Call it `BridgeRecord`. Then you must specify the range of each index. The first index has values ranging from 1 through 23, corresponding to the number of bridges. The second index has values ranging from 1 through 5, corresponding to the number of inspection teams.

TIP: You know that BridgeRecord is a numeric array variable — as it should be — because its name does not end with a dollar sign.

An array is defined in True BASIC by a `DIM` statement (`DIM` is an abbreviation for Dimension) that specifies the name of the array variable, the size of the array (that is, the number of indices), and the range of each index. Here is what your `DIM` statement should look like:

```
DIM BridgeRecord(1 to 23, 1 to 5)
```

If you wish, you can use a colon (:) instead of the word "`to`" to separate index values.

Stop a minute and think about what you have done. You have created a new type of data structure, an array variable, that can store many numeric values, up to 115 of them in this case. The array has two numeric indices, one referring to bridges and the other to inspection teams. An array of this size is often called a *two-dimensional array*. The value of one index ranges from 1 to 23, the other index from 1 to 5. Each storage location in the array is called an *element* of the array and is identified by two index numbers. The initial value of every element in a numeric array is zero.

It may help you to visualize an array by thinking of it as a table with 23 rows and 5 columns, as shown in Fig. 3.2. This array diagram shows only 10 rows to save book space, the array actually has 23 rows

0	0	0	0	0
0	0	0	0	0
0	0	0	0	0
0	0	0	0	0
0	0	0	0	0
0	0	0	0	0
0	0	0	0	0
0	0	0	0	0
0	0	0	0	0
0	0	0	0	0

Figure 3.2 *Part of empty array, showing 10 rows and 5 columns.*

To refer to the element of the array that holds the natural frequency of bridge 5 measured by team 2, use the notation

```
BridgeRecord(5, 2)
```

where the first index identifies a particular bridge and the second index identifies a particular inspection team.

If you want to assign a frequency value to that element, use the following assignment statement:

```
LET BridgeRecord(5, 2) = 6.1
```

This statement means that bridge 5 had a natural frequency of 6.1 hertz when measured by team 2, and that value is stored in the appropriate element of the

BridgeRecord array variable. Fig. 3.3 shows your array diagram with that single score placed in the proper element.

0	0	0	0	0
0	0	0	0	0
0	0	0	0	0
0	0	0	0	0
0	6.1	0	0	0
0	0	0	0	0
0	0	0	0	0
0	0	0	0	0
0	0	0	0	0
0	0	0	0	0

Figure 3.3 *Array with single frequency in element (5, 2).*

Creating a One-Dimensional String Array Variable

Before continuing this discussion of bridge frequencies, I need to tell you a little more about arrays. In the preceding example you used a two-dimensional array. You can also define a simpler data structure, a one-dimensional array with only one index. If you think of the two-dimensional array as a table, you might think of the one-dimensional array as a list. It is even possible to have an array variable with three or more dimensions — they aren't discussed in this book.

While the elements in your `BridgeRecord` array contain numeric values, you can just as easily define an array that contains string values. All you have to do is specify a dollar sign as the last character in the array name. Here is an example of a one-dimensional array that can store a list of 100 names:

```
DIM Name$(1 to 100)
```

How long can each name be? The maximum length of a string in True BASIC is 65,528 characters (this value is for the DOS version, in the Mac version it is much larger) so there is really no practical limit on the length of a name.

TIP: As you can see, the array variable is a powerful and useful data structure but there is one thing it *cannot* do; it cannot store a combination of numeric and string values in the same array. Each element in a numeric array must be a number, each element in a string array must be a string.

3.2 A SIMPLE FOR LOOP

As you think about the process of entering bridge frequencies into an array, you begin to realize how many input statements are needed. In fact, 115 input statements are needed to enter all frequency measurements of all bridges. Essentially the same statement must be written over and over again.

A better way to accomplish this task of entering data is to use the process of *looping*. In the next example program, I introduce a simple kind of loop structure that works especially well with an indexed variable.

Exactly what do I mean by a loop? I mean a program structure that repeats a block of one or more statements over and over again. How many times does the loop repeat? That depends on the conditions you choose when you write the loop. In the case of the loop structure I am introducing here, the loop repeats a fixed number of times based on the index values. In other loop structures, the number of times the loop repeats is determined by the computer program.

What does indentation of statements have to do with a loop? It usually makes a loop easier to read but that is all, it has no direct effect on the loop.

The FOR and NEXT Statements

A pair of statements, the `FOR` statement and the `NEXT` statement, are often used to create a loop that executes a given number of times. Look at a very simple example:

```
! Example Program 3-1
! Demonstrate the use of a FOR loop.

FOR Count = 1 to 5          ! top of loop
   PRINT Count;
NEXT Count                  ! bottom of loop
END
```

The following program output is produced:

```
 1  2  3  4  5
```

Let me explain how the program works. You need to read this information carefully, probably more than once.

The numeric variable `Count` is called the *control variable*. At the top of the loop — the `FOR` statement — it is given an *initial value* of 1. The indented statement is called the *loop body*. In many cases, the loop body contains more than one statement. After the loop body statement — `PRINT Count` — is executed, the `NEXT` statement at the bottom of the loop returns program control to the `FOR` statement at the top of the loop.

At this point, the control variable `Count` is automatically incremented by one to a value of 2. The value of `Count` is now compared to the *final value* of 5 and looping continues because `Count` is less than or equal to 5. The computer program makes this decision itself without any help on your part.

When `Count` reaches the value of 6, the `FOR` statement notes that this value exceeds the final value of 5 and looping is stopped. Program execution then continues with the statement following the `NEXT` statement — in this case, the `END` statement.

That's not so hard to understand, is it?

TIP: There are other options for the `FOR` loop that are not discussed in this chapter. They are explained in the manual and in the help files.

Challenge Problem 3-1

As mentioned in a preceding section, arrays can hold string values instead of numeric values. Write a program that creates an array containing the names of a six-member bridge inspection team. Remember to dimension your array — I suggest you name it `Team$`. You decide whether to store first names or last names or complete names. Use a `FOR` loop to enter names from the keyboard. This is just a practice problem, the array of names is deleted when the program ends.

3.3 THE BRIDGE INSPECTION, PART I

Now let's use the `FOR` loop for a more practical purpose, to assign natural frequencies to a bridge in the previously discussed array `BridgeRecord`. Example Program 3-2 prompts the user to enter the measured frequency values for bridge 9:

```
! Example Program 3-2
! Ask the user to enter the natural frequency
! measurements for bridge 9.

DIM BridgeRecord(1:23, 1:5)
LET Bridge = 9
PRINT "Frequency measurements for bridge"; Bridge
FOR Team = 1 to 5
   PRINT "Measurement of team"; Team;
   INPUT BridgeRecord(Bridge, Team)
NEXT Team
END
```

Note that the question marks after each prompt are created by the `INPUT` statement.

The following screen output is displayed when the program is executed:

```
Frequency measurements for bridge 9
Measurement of team 1 ? 6.5
Measurement of team 2 ? 6.7
Measurement of team 3 ? 6.8
Measurement of team 4 ? 6.5
Measurement of team 5 ? 6.9
```

The amount of work required to enter scores is the same as if five simple variables had been used, but the program is significantly shorter. Fig. 3.4 shows your array diagram with the scores for skater 9 entered.

0	0	0	0	0
0	0	0	0	0
0	0	0	0	0
0	0	0	0	0
0	0	0	0	0
0	0	0	0	0
0	0	0	0	0
0	0	0	0	0
6.5	6.7	6.8	6.5	6.9
0	0	0	0	0

Figure 3.4 *Array with scores entered in row 9.*

This program has filled only one row of the array `BridgeRecord` with frequency measurements. What are the contents of the other rows? All other elements contain zeroes, the usual initial value for any numeric variable. How do you place scores in the other rows? You write a program with another loop that repeats the loop in Example Program 3-2 for every row in the array `BridgeRecord`. In other words, the program has one loop within another loop. Here is what that program looks like:

```
! Example Program 3-3
! Ask user to enter the natural frequency
! measurements for all bridges.

DIM BridgeRecord(1 to 23, 1 to 5)
FOR Bridge = 1 to 23                          !top of outer loop
    PRINT "Frequencies for bridge"; Skater
    FOR Team = 1 to 5                         !top of inner loop

        PRINT "Measurement by team"; Team;
        INPUT BridgeRecord(Bridge, Team)
```

```
    NEXT Team                         !bottom of inner loop
    PRINT        !Advance a line for the next bridge
NEXT Bridge                           !bottom of outer loop
END
```

Note carefully that the FOR loop for the 5 teams — the inner loop — is totally enclosed by the FOR loop for the bridges — the outer loop. Proper indentation helps to make the structure clearer. The user must enter 115 scores as the program runs. You have done nothing to make the data entry problem shorter or easier but the program length has increased only slightly from the length of the single-bridge program. Just a small part of the program output is shown:

```
Frequencies for bridge 1
Measurement by team 1 ? 3.7
Measurement by team 2 ? 3.9
Measurement by team 3 ? 3.8
Measurement by team 4 ? 4.0
Measurement by team 5 ? 3.5

Frequencies for bridge 2
Measurement by team 1 ? 5.2
Measurement by team 2 ? 5.5
Measurement by team 3 ? 5.7
.
.
```

This technique of using two loops, one within the other, is often referred to as *nesting loops*. You will see it used in other example programs.

Challenge Problem 3-2

Mathematicians often use a special two-dimensional numeric array called the *identity matrix*. Matrix is just a mathematical name for an array. The identity matrix must have the same number of rows and columns, sometimes called a *square array*. All elements in the identity matrix have a value of zero except elements along the principle diagonal, these elements have a value of one. The *principle diagonal* runs from the upper left corner to the lower right corner of the array. Here is an identity matrix with 3 rows and 3 columns:

```
1  0  0
0  1  0
0  0  1
```

Write a program that creates a 3 x 3 identity matrix — that is, with 3 rows and 3 columns — and displays this matrix on the screen. Be sure your program actually creates an array, I suggest denoting that array by the name Identity. You will probably need one pair of nested FOR loops to assign values to the array and another pair to display the array.

WHAT YOU HAVE LEARNED

Example Program 3-3 is laborious to use because it requires all 115 measurements to be entered one by one from the keyboard. If the individual measurements had been entered into a text file by the teams as they made their inspections, it is easy to write a program that reads scores from a text file rather than from the keyboard. Be patient, I discuss that topic in Chapter 5.

Topic	Page
Two-dimensional numeric array	32
Storing information in an array	33
One-dimensional string array	34
Looping and the FOR loop	35
How to nest one FOR loop inside another	38

Figure 3.5—*What you have learned in Chapter 3.*

Testing and Debugging

Every program you write must be thoroughly tested. In this chapter, I discuss how to design a new program, write it, and then test it. The task of testing is vital but often overlooked — a program should not be considered finished until it has been carefully tested.

Your goal should be to write programs that contain no errors. It is probably an impossible goal to attain but you should be able to reduce the number of errors to a minimum. At the same time, you must learn how to find errors and remove them from your programs. This process is called *debugging*.

4.1 PROGRAM CREATION

This is a good time to discuss some steps you must follow when creating a new program. You have already learned the mechanics of editing and running a True BASIC program. Now you are ready to consider program design and to learn about program testing.

Program Design

If it does nothing else, I hope this discussion will convince you that it is a waste of time to sit down at a computer and write a program without any thought about program design. You can obviously write a two or three line program without much thought. As your source program approaches the length of a page, however, you need guidance from an outline, either written or mental. I strongly recommend a written outline.

Choosing an Algorithm

Most computer programs are designed to solve a problem. Before starting to write the program, be sure you understand the problem. It's surprising how often people don't. Then plan how your program will solve that problem. The method of solution is called an *algorithm*. The algorithm you choose should be simple and efficient.

How do you learn algorithms? There is no simple answer — there is no such thing as a magic list of algorithms that solve all problems. To learn about algorithms, you read books and articles, you read programs written by others, and you discuss methods of solution with other programmers. If you choose a poor algorithm, you may end up with a poor program.

Frankly, I can't give you a formula for writing perfect programs. I can tell you from my own experience, however, that a well-thought-out outline and an effective algorithm usually produce a well-written program that works. Your motto should be: **Plan first, program later**.

4.2 FINDING ERRORS

Having written a computer program, the next step is to find out whether it runs. As you execute each statement, True BASIC checks the statement syntax and won't let you move ahead until the statement syntax is correct. Remember to use the manual or the help files to verify statement syntax.

The syntax of every statement may be correct but the program produces incorrect results or no results. What is wrong? What do you do? The procedure you must follow is called *debugging*, the process of finding and correcting program errors called *bugs*. These errors are often errors in logic.

Playing Computer

One of the best methods for finding errors is to read through a computer program, pretending that you are the computer. In your mind, you make all the calculations and decisions that would normally be made by the computer. Many simple errors are revealed.

This method is easy to understand and to apply, but it can be tedious. You will find it most useful for examining small sections of a program. In fact, it is the method all of us turn to instinctively when programs don't run. You can make better progress if you write down intermediate results on paper, in a systematic format. If complicated arithmetic calculations are involved, use a hand calculator to speed up the process.

In spite of its limitations, try this method first. It's a natural way to find errors if a program is not working properly.

Temporary PRINT Statements

Beginning programmers often say to me, "I know that the value of variable `X` at this point in the program is 15.2, but when I make a calculation using `X` and print the results, they are wrong." My response is, "How do you know that the value of `X` is 15.2?"

One way to answer that question is to put a temporary `PRINT` statement in your program and see what the value of `X` actually is at the point of calculation. It is surprising how often it is different from what you thought it would be!

It is not unusual to insert half a dozen temporary `PRINT` statements in a program before finding an error. Sometimes it is helpful to include a label in the `PRINT` statement to help identify its location.

For example, the statement

```
PRINT "In the Report section: X ="; X
```

identifies the variable being displayed and the program section where it has this value. A single `PRINT` statement can display the values of several variables. For example, the statement

```
PRINT "After first pass: Index,Sum = ";Index; Sum
```

displays the values of both `Index` and `Sum`. You must, of course, remember to delete these temporary `PRINT` statements after you have found the error.

The DO TRACE Command

True BASIC has a powerful debugging capability in the `DO TRACE` command. You should learn how to use it. This command lets you execute a program, statement by statement, in slow motion and display the values of selected variables. The program is displayed in a *program window*, selected variable values are displayed in another window called the *variables window*, and program output appears in a third window called the *output window*.

To get the full benefit of this command, you must execute it from the command line, not from a menu. Your first concern is whether your computer knows where to find the `TRACE` program. While you could type in the full path name each time you enter the command, there is a better way. Create a new, empty True BASIC program containing the statement line:

```
ALIAS do, c:\tbasic\tbdo\,""
```

and name this program STARTUP.TRU. While you are at it, you might add a second statement line as follows:

```
ALIAS help, c:\tbasic\tbhelp\, ""
```

Program `STARTUP.TRU` should be saved in your current directory, the directory that contains `HELLO.EXE`. The syntax I have used assumes that your True BASIC system is in a directory named TBASIC on disk drive C — if not, use the correct path name.

What do these two statement lines do? They tell the computer that if you try to execute either a `DO` command or a `HELP` command, it should look first in directory `C:\TBASIC\TBDO\` or directory `C:\TBASIC\TBHELP\`. If the computer can't find the program you want there, it should try the current directory (denoted by ""). This `STARTUP` file will keep you out of trouble and let you execute `DO TRACE` commands from the command line. By the way, I should mention that this file is named `STARTUP` because it executes immediately and automatically when the True BASIC system is started.

The Command window is always visible on a DOS screen, but not necessarily on a Macintosh screen. If you are using a Mac, select the Command item from the Windows menu and a command window with the Ok. prompt appears. If you are using a Mac, remember that its syntax for path names is a little different from the DOS syntax — colons replace backslashes and spaces are allowed in names.

Returning to the `DO TRACE` command itself, the proper syntax is

```
Ok. DO TRACE, option (variables)
```

where I have shown the Ok. prompt as well as the command syntax.

The argument *option* may be one of four choices: "step", "slow", "fast", or "break." I almost always use the option "step" — it is by far the most useful choice. This option executes a single program statement each time the space bar is pressed, allowing you to control the speed of stepping through the program. See the *True BASIC Reference Manual* for information on the other options, and on how to handle programs containing external procedures (discussed in Chapter 8).

The argument *variables* is a list of program variables separated from one another by commas. As many as eight different variables can be included in the list, their values are displayed and can be monitored.

The technique for using the `DO TRACE` command is simple. Enter the command from the command line, even if you are using a computer with a mouse. Specify an option of "step." Select a few variables whose values you want to watch. Then start pressing the space bar and single-step through the program.

Here is a simple example program that you can try yourself:

```
LET Sum = 0
FOR Count = 1 to 5
    PRINT Count;
    LET Sum = Sum + Count
NEXT Count
PRINT
PRINT Sum
END
```

You know from looking at the program that it will produce a list of the numbers from 1 to 5 on one line and the sum of these five numbers (15) on the next line. Instead of running this program in the normal manner, enter the following ìtraceî command:

```
Ok. DO TRACE, step (Count, Sum)
```

Your command tells the computer to single-step through the program, keeping track of and displaying the changing values of `Count` and `Sum`. You will see three windows:

- The *program window* with the current statement highlighted.
- The *variables window* showing the current values of variables `Count` and `Sum`.
- The *output window* showing program output as it is generated.

Each time you press the space bar, one or more of the windows will change its display. Itís almost like magic, peeking inside the program this way and watching whatís happening. Try it yourself — I think you'll be impressed.

So that's how the `DO TRACE` command works — it is indeed a powerful tool. While it is possible to execute this command by selecting it from the Options menu, I think that's a mistake because you lose the ability to specify variable values and watch them as they change. I recommend that you always execute `DO TRACE` from the command line.

Challenge Problem 4-1

Use the `DO TRACE` command to single-step through a program you have written. I suggest using Challenge Program 3-2. Display the values of at least two variables as you step through the program. It pays to become familiar with the `DO TRACE` command before you have to use in an emergency when a program you have written yields incorrect results.

4.3 PROGRAM TESTING

You finally have a program that runs and produces reasonable results. Are you finished? Some programmers may think so but they are dead wrong. You still need to test your program under as many different conditions as possible.

If your program restricts input to a particular range of values, try entering values at the limits of that range. For example, if the input must be between 0 and 100, be sure to test inputs of 0, 100, and maybe 101. Another good test is to let someone else run your program and ask them to try to make it fail. If they can make it fail, you are not finished, your program still contains errors. As they say in the computer business, your program is not robust!

Professional programmers consider they are only half way through a project when they have finished the source program and it runs. Testing a program often takes just as long as writing it, and preferably should include several people besides the author.

WHAT YOU HAVE LEARNED

Believe it or not, the most important lesson you can learn from this chapter is the need to test computer programs. The need to debug a program is obvious because a program that won't run has very little value. The need for thorough testing is not as obvious.

Once you have debugged your program and produced some accurate results, there is a tendency to stop and say the program is finished. Nothing is further from the truth. I have seen many programs written by programmers — both beginners and those with considerable experience — that were tested only briefly and when put into use, failed miserably. You must thoroughly test every program you write. It is probably the least observed and most important step in program development.

Topic	**Page**
Learning to design programs	41
Playing computer	42
Displaying values of variables	42
Using the TRACE facility programs	43
Testing, testing, testing	45

Figure 4.1*—What you have learned in Chapter 4.*

Reading and Writing Text Files

Programs in this book use only text files which are defined in Chapter 1 as collections of readable text characters. You can assume throughout the book that the word *file* means a text file. Just as you write characters on the screen and read them from the keyboard, you can also write them on a file and read them from a file. Text files contain characters. Any True BASIC computer program can access one or more files.

5.1 USING A TEXT FILE

You must take the three following steps to use a file in one of your programs:

1. Open the desired file for reading or writing and associate a True BASIC file number — often called a *channel number* — with the file's DOS or Mac path name. Opening a file makes it available for use in a program.
2. Use a file version of the `PRINT` statement to write information on the file; a file version of the `INPUT` statement to read information from the file.
3. Close the file when you are through using it.

That all sounds pretty simple, doesn't it? And it really isn't difficult. Before discussing these three steps, let's talk about files a little more.

How to Picture a File

What image of a file do you have in your mind? What do you think it looks like? Let me give you a description and mental picture that I have found helpful.

- A text file contains lines of text. I use line in the broadest sense: a single character, a number stored as numeric digit characters and maybe a decimal point, a 2000-character string. Every character in the line must be one of the set of 256 ASCII characters (see Appendix F) and is stored on the file using an ASCII code.

- An end-of-line marker (EOLN) appears at the end of each line. This EOLN marker consists of two characters, the carriage return (ASCII value 13) and the line feed (ASCII value 10). They are non-printing characters but when a file is displayed by many text editors, these two characters cause each file line to be displayed as a separate screen line.
- An end-of-file marker (EOF) appears after the last line of the file. A non-printing character with the ASCII value of 26 — called *control-Z* — is often used for this purpose. The EOF marker can be detected in a program by the `End` function, using the notation `End #N` where `N` is the file or channel number.

Now you can draw yourself a picture of a file. Imagine a file containing the following four lines:

```
-20.7
second place
z
robin
```

Fig. 5.1 shows an imaginary section of this file's disk track, highly magnified. Remember that this is just a mental image, the real disk track has only invisible magnetic regions representing the bits that contain the information stored on the file.

```
-20.7  EOLN  second place  EOLN  z  EOLN  robin  EOLN EOF
```

***Figure 5.1**—Section of a file track on disk.*

Opening a File

An `OPEN` statement in True BASIC opens files. It has two required parameters that specify the True BASIC file or channel number and the DOS or Mac path name. It has three optional parameters that specify how the file is accessed, whether the file is old or new, and the type of file.

In DOS and also in Windows, the statement

```
OPEN #1: name "C:\JIM", access input, create old, org text
```

opens a text file whose path name is "C:\JIM" as file number 1. This file is opened to be used for input — that is, for reading information from an old or existing text file.

It's kind of a long statement, isn't it? With some versions of True BASIC, you can use the continuation character — the ampersand (&) — to extend a statement over two or more lines. Here is the same statement written on two lines:

```
OPEN #1: name "C:\JIM.REC", access output, &
& create old, org text
```

The first character in every line except the first line must be an ampersand, the last character in every line except the last continuation line must be an ampersand. There must be at least one space between each ampersand and the character closest to it on the same line.

TIP: Check your version of True BASIC to see if it supports the continuation character.

In many programs using only a single file, the file is opened as #1. It doesn't have to be number 1, that's just common practice. The file can be assigned any number from 1 through 99. If you open more than one file in a program, each file must have a different channel number.

Why specify a path name, not just a file name? Put yourself in the computer's place. To open a file, you must know where it is stored. That means knowing the disk drive letter or name, the chain of directories or folders leading to the file, and the file name. All this information is provided by the path name.

Other File Statements

There are two other file statements that are often used in conjunction with the `OPEN` statement. True BASIC has an invisible *file pointer* that can point to any position in a file. The file pointer indicates the position where the next character will be written or read. Two `RESET` statements move this pointer. The statement

```
RESET #1: begin
```

sets the file pointer to the beginning of file #1 (before the first character) while the statement

```
RESET #1: end
```

sets the file pointer to point at the end of the same file (after the last character).

TIP: The beginning and end of an empty file are the same point — an obvious statement that sometimes causes confusion.

The `ERASE` statement does just what its name implies, it erases the contents of an existing file. In the process, it sets the file pointer — showing where the next item of data will be written — to the beginning of the file. See Example Program 5-1.

Access Mode: Default Outin

The default mode is "outin" meaning that the file is opened for both output and input — writing and reading. This is the most common access mode.

If the access mode is "input", the file is opened for input from the disk file to the program. The file is opened for reading only and information cannot be written on the file. If you try to do so, you will receive an error message. You might use this mode to prevent unauthorized writing on a file.

If the access mode of the file is "output", the file is opened for output from the program to the disk file. The file is opened for writing only and information cannot be read from the file. There is seldom any reason for opening a file in this mode.

Create Mode: Default Old

If the create mode of the file is "old", the default value, the program looks for an existing file with that path name. If none exists, you receive an error message.

If the create mode is "new", the program tries to open a new file. An existing file with the same path name produces an error.

The create mode of "newold" means that the program uses an old file if it exists and if not, it opens a new file. This mode should be specified if you are uncertain whether or not a file exists.

Organization: Default Text

The organization of a file, abbreviated "org", specifies the type of file. True BASIC supports many file types: text, record, random, stream, and binary or byte files. You will use only text files in this book. Since that is the default organization type, you do not need to specify an organization parameter.

It is important to remember that you can start writing only at the beginning of a new text file or at the end of an existing text file. You can also erase an existing file and write on it again. There is no way you can start writing somewhere in the middle of a text file. When reading a file, you can start only at the beginning of an existing text file. These are limitations of text files that are often not fully appreciated but you must understand them.

Example Statements

Here are some example statements. The variable `N` contains the channel number, the variable `Path$` contains the file's path name. The statement

```
OPEN #N: name Path$, access input
```

opens file Path$ for input as file #N. There is no need to specify the create mode because the default is "old." Once again, "input" means reading information from the file. The only place you can start reading is at the beginning of a file and you can continue reading right through to the end. Of course, you cannot read an empty file. Trying to read past the end of a file or trying to read a file that does not exist causes an error.

TIP: Trying to read past the end of a file is the same as trying to read the EOF marker — you can't do it.

The statement

```
OPEN #N: name Path$, access outin, create newold
```

opens file Path$ for either input or output as file #N. If a new file is specified, information can be written on it. Reading a new file produces no output because the file is empty. If a file with that path name already exists, information can be read from it. Note that "outin" is the default value and thus the access parameter may be omitted.

TIP: After you become familiar with the OPEN statement syntax, you can omit parameters with default values.

If you wish to overwrite the contents of an existing file, use the following pair of statements:

```
OPEN #N: name Path$, create newold
ERASE #N
```

You will start writing new information at the beginning of the file.

On the other hand, if you wish to add information to the contents of an existing file, use this pair of statements:

```
OPEN #N: name Path$, create newold
RESET #N: end
```

Writing now starts at the end of the existing file.

The preceding statements all use variables for the path name and the channel number. By now, I expect you recognize that this is not required, a string value or even a string expression can just as well be used for the path name and a numeric value for the channel number. For example, if the path name of a Macintosh file happens to be "Boot Disk:True Basic:test data" and you wish to open it for input as file #1, the proper statement is

```
OPEN #1: name "Boot Disk:True BASIC:text data", access input
```

Remember that spaces are significant in Mac file names, and colons are used instead of backslashes for separators. Sometimes a file name is not recognized because someone has inadvertently added leading or trailing spaces to the name. These spaces must be removed before the file name can be used in a program. Look up the `Trim$` function in your manual or a help file or Appendix E.

Closing a File

When you are finished using a file in your program, it is good practice to close it. The required statement is

```
CLOSE #N
```

Why is it desirable to close files? There are two good reasons. Sometimes you may need to open additional files but are unable to do so. Several files may already be open but not in use; new files cannot be opened because the operating system limits the total number of files open at any time. How many files can be open simultaneously? It really depends on the configuration of your particular system, but often a number like 6 or 8 open files is the maximum. Remember that an application may also use some file channels.

The other reason for closing files is that many operating systems use buffered output when writing on a file. This means that any file output is placed in a buffer — a reserved section of memory — and only when the buffer is full is the buffered information written on the file. Buffering improves the speed of writing on disk, a much slower process than writing in memory.

Most programs empty all file buffers when the program stops, but once in a while this is not done (for example, when the power fails) and information you thought had been written on the disk is left in a buffer. Imagine the problems that can cause! So many programmers — and I include myself in that group — close a file after writing on it is finished. Closing the file automatically writes the buffer contents on the disk.

TIP: Always close a file after you have finished writing on it — it just makes good sense to remove one possible source of errors.

5.2 WRITING ON A TEXT FILE

A modified form of the `PRINT` statement is used to write information on a disk file. The syntax is

```
PRINT #1: "multimeter"
```

where the file was opened as file #1 and the string value shown is written on the file. Instead of a value, a variable or an expression can be used. The channel or file number can also be specified by a variable as in the following program fragment:

```
LET N = 1
LET Item$ = "multimeter"
PRINT #N: Item$
```

You can include several items in the `PRINT #` statement, separated by commas, but I recommend that unless there are special reasons for doing so, you write only one item per `PRINT` statement.

TIP: The advantage of a single item is that each value written on the file is written on a its own line, separated from its neighbors by EOLN markers. This is the first assumption I make when reading a foreign text file whose structure is unknown.

If you use a variable, it can be either a string variable (as shown) or a numeric variable. In both cases, the value is written on the file in ASCII code. This is an important statement, often not well understood.

Everything you write on a text file is encoded using the ASCII code. For example, you can write a digit character on the file as a string and then read it off the file as a number. More about that later.

Here is an example program that creates the file, shown in Fig. 5.1, on your floppy disk in drive A. If your floppy disk drive is B, use that letter instead. If you have no floppy disk drive, create the file on your fixed disk.

```
! Example Program 5-1
! Write four values on the file EX5-1.DAT
! in the root directory of the disk in drive A.
! The default access mode is "outin."

OPEN #1: name "A:\EX5-1.DAT", create new
ERASE #1 !in case it already contains data
PRINT #1: -20.7
PRINT #1: "second place"
PRINT #1: "z"
PRINT #1: "robin"
CLOSE #1
PRINT "File EX5-1.DAT has been written."
END
```

This program produces a single line of output:

```
File EX5-1.DAT has been written.
```

That single line of output is important, however, because it tells the user what has happened. Beginning programmers expect to see program output, if they don't, they start to worry that their program is not running properly.

The first value of -20.7 is a numeric value but it is written on the file as a string of ASCII character codes. Remember that this is the only kind of information you can write on a text file. The remaining three items are string values and thus must be enclosed in quotation marks. Note that each item is written on a separate line of the file.

TIP: The `ERASE` statement removes any previous contents from an existing file. If not needed, you are writing on an empty file or creating a new file, in which case the statement does no harm.

Challenge Problem 5-1

Write a program to create a new text file. Ask the user for the complete path name of the new file and assign that name to a variable named `PathName$`. Open a file with this name by including `PathName$` in the `OPEN` statement. Write 10 lines of text on the new file using a loop and then close the file. Be sure to display a message telling the user what has happened.

5.3 READING FROM A TEXT FILE

You must also learn how to read files, either files that you have created or files written by others. Programs more often read information from existing files than create new files.

A modified version of the `INPUT` statement is used for reading from a file and has the following syntax:

```
INPUT #N: Item$
```

As before, the channel number is the value of `N` and the value read from the file is stored in the variable `Item$`.

As an example, the following program reads the file that you wrote in the preceding section You know that file has exactly four items in it so you can read it with a `FOR` loop that loops four times. Here is the program:

```
! Example Program 5-2
! Read and display four values in file EX5-1.DAT
! in the root directory of the disk in drive A.

OPEN #1: name "A:\EX5-1.DAT", access input
PRINT "Contents of file EX5-1.DAT"
PRINT
FOR Count = 1 to 4
    INPUT #1: Item$
    PRINT Item$
NEXT Count
CLOSE #1
END
```

The following output is produced:

```
Contents of file EX5-1.DAT

-20.7
second place
z
robin
```

Not much is needed here in the way of explanation. The file is opened for input, the create mode by default is "old." Each item is read from the file, line by line, into the variable `Item$` and then displayed on the screen. Once again, a displayed comment tells the user which file is being read. The file is closed after reading, probably unnecessary but it does no harm.

TIP: Reading a file with a `FOR` loop is generally not a good idea — you usually don't know the number of lines in a file. In this case, I use a `FOR` loop because that is the only kind of loop you know about and I know I wrote only four lines in the file.

The usual situation is the need to write a program that can read a file with an unknown number of lines or items. You will learn how to do that later in the chapter when I introduce a method for detecting the end of a file.

Another INPUT Statement: LINE INPUT

Here is a useful variation of the `INPUT` statement that you have not yet used. The `LINE INPUT` statement reads a complete line of text from the keyboard, stopping only when the Return key is pressed. The `LINE INPUT #` statement reads a complete line of text from a file, stopping only when the EOLN marker is encountered. The proper syntax for the latter statement is

```
LINE INPUT #N: Line$
```

Why is this statement — the file version — so useful when reading files? When you write a string value on a file, it is written on a single line. Thus the string

```
"William Bankhead, Jr."
```

is written on a file exactly as shown but without the quotation marks. When you try to read that line from the file with an `INPUT #` statement, the program notes the comma and considers it a separator between two string values. Thus only the string William Bankhead — without the Jr. — is read. If you read the line with the `LINE INPUT #` statement, however, the entire line is read properly.

There are limitations on the use of both `LINE INPUT` statements — they can only read a single variable and it must be a string variable. See your manual or a help file for more details. If you have a choice when reading files, use the `LINE INPUT #` statement to read complete lines.

TIP: When reading single strings, develop the habit of using the `LINE INPUT` statement instead of the `INPUT` statement.

Here is a little experiment to test your understanding of reading text files. Use the True BASIC editor to modify the file EX5-1.DAT by placing a comma between the words "second" and "place." The modified file contents should look as follows:

```
-20.7
second, place
z
robin
```

Now read that file with Example Program 5-2. What kind of results do you get? Can you explain what happened? Modify Example Program 5-2 by replacing the `INPUT #` statement with a `LINE INPUT #` statement. Run the program and read the file again. What do you see this time? Do you understand why it is often better to use the `LINE INPUT #` statement in spite of its limitations?

ANSWER: The second value read from the file is the word "second" because the comma is interpreted as the end of the second item. The third value read is then "place" and the fourth value "z." Poor "robin" never gets read at all!

Numbers or Strings?

Let's go back to that old but bothersome question: When is a sequence of digits a number and when is it a string? Consider the first value on the file, the character sequence -20.7. If you read this file value with the statement

```
INPUT #1, Item
```

you are reading the value into a numeric variable and it is stored there as a number. You can use the numeric variable `Item` in arithmetic expressions.

On the other hand, if you read this file value with the statement

```
INPUT #1, Item$
```

you are reading the value into a string variable and it is stored there as a string, a sequence of ASCII characters. You cannot use the string variable `Item$` in arithmetic expressions.

Reviewing the situation, *everything is written on text files as ASCII characters.* If an appropriate sequence of characters is read into a numeric variable, it is stored as a number and behaves like a number. If any sequence of characters is read into a string variable, it is stored as a string and behaves like a string.

Note the word "appropriate" in the preceding paragraph. If you read a string of characters that does not represent a number and try to store it in a numeric variable, you will get an error.

Finding the End of a File

Most of the time when you read a file, you have no idea how many items it contains. When writing a general file-reading program, you need some way to detect the end of the file. Thankfully, True BASIC provides such a test, using the function `End #`.

You may remember that I introduced a function named `Sqr` in Chapter 2 that has — or as they say in the computer world, returns — a numerical value. The `End #` function is similar but different, it is called a logical function and returns a value of either true or false.

Think of an imaginary file pointer that moves through a file from character to character as the file is being read. This pointer always points at the next item to be read. When that next item is the EOF marker, the `End #` function returns a value of true. At all other times the `End #` function returns a value of false.

TIP: Even though you can't see it, the file pointer is a useful and important concept.

5.4 LOOPING: The DO Loop

The `End #` logical function can be used to control the behavior of a more general loop structure called a `DO` loop. It allows the number of loop repetitions to be controlled by user input or by a decision of the program itself.

Two new statements are needed, a `DO` statement at the top of the loop and a `LOOP` statement at the bottom of the loop. All program statements between these two statements make up the loop body. Let's look at a revised version of Example Program 5-2 and then discuss how it works.

```
! Example Program 5-3
! Read and display the values in a file
! whose path name is specified by the user.

INPUT PROMPT "Path name? ": Path$
OPEN #5: name Path$  !Assume the file exists
PRINT
DO until End #5
     LINE INPUT #5, Item$
     PRINT Item$
LOOP
CLOSE #5
END
```

If the user enter the path name "A:\EX5-1.DAT", the output is exactly the same as that of Example Program 5-2 and is shown again here:

```
Path Name? A:\EX5-1.DAT

-20.7
second, place
z
robin
```

The loop is executed the first time because `End #5` is false — the imaginary file pointer points at the beginning of a newly opened file that contains data. An item on the file is read and the pointer advances to the next item. The `LOOP` statement returns control to the `DO` statement at the top of the loop.

Each time the `DO` statement is executed, the value of function `END #5` is checked. If it is still false, the loop continues; if it becomes true — because the pointer now points at the EOF marker — control is transferred to the first statement after the `LOOP` statement, in this case, the `CLOSE #5` statement. The EOF marker itself is never read, that would cause an error.

Why did I use a channel number of 5? Just to get you used to the idea that any channel number up to 99 is allowed.

Challenge Problem 5-2

Write a program that reads any text file of reasonable length. Enter the path name of the file from the keyboard. If you don't know what file to choose, read the file created in Challenge Problem 5-1. Your program should use both the `End` function and the `LINE INPUT #` statement. Display on the screen the file path name, a blank line, and then the entire contents of the file.

5.5 USING A MEMORY DATA FILE

Computer users normally think of disk files when the word "file" is mentioned. True BASIC does provide a way, however, to create a file in memory. Why would you ever want to use a memory file?

A memory data file is useful for storing a small group of items that may be used over and over again in a program, such as the 12 months of the year or the 16 colors available on your monitor screen. The contents of a memory file are created when the program is written and cannot be changed by the program user. The values are kept in memory, can be quickly and easily accessed, and can be used many times in the program.

DATA Statement

DATA statements are used to store string or numeric values in memory. The individual values are separated from each other by commas. If a string value contains any characters except alphabetic characters or digits, it should be enclosed in quotation marks. There can be one or more DATA statements in a program. Here is an example:

```
DATA Sunday, Monday, Tuesday, Wednesday
DATA Thursday, Friday, Saturday
```

DATA statements are not executable statements and can be placed anywhere in a program before the END statement. When you run a True BASIC program, one of the first things the computer does is look for DATA statements. If it finds any, it writes their values to a reserved section of memory where they are available to the program. As mentioned previously, the only way you can change these values is by editing the program and running it again.

READ Statement

One or more READ statements are used to assign these stored values to variables. The READ statement, as its name implies, reads a data value and assigns it to a variable. The variable is often an array variable. Data values are read in the order in which they appear in DATA statements, beginning with the first DATA statement. Here is an example program.

```
! Example Program 5-4.
! Read the days of the week from DATA
! statements and assign them to an array.

DIM DayOfWeek$ (1:7)
RESTORE  ! See the following note in the text.
LET Index = 0
DO until end data
   LET Index = Index + 1
   READ DayOfWeek$(Index)
LOOP

! Display the array contents
! just to check the results.
FOR Count = 1 to 7
    PRINT DayOfWeek$(Count)
NEXT Count

DATA Sunday, Monday, Tuesday, Wednesday
DATA Thursday, Friday, Saturday
END
```

I need to explain the new RESTORE statement. When executed, this statement moves the position of the first read — sometimes described as moving the position of an imaginary data pointer — to the beginning of the first DATA statement. In this example, the statement doesn't change anything but does no harm.

If the example program was part of a larger program and you had to read the memory file — the DATA statements — several times, the RESTORE statement must be executed each time before you start to read the data. Otherwise, the data pointer may be moved past the end of the last data statement and an out-of-data error occurs.

If there is any question, include a RESTORE statement in a program that uses DATA statements. It won't cause any problems if it's not needed.

Challenge Problem 5-3

Write another version of the program for Challenge Problem 3-1 but this time read the six names of the team members from a memory data file. As a check, add code to print out the six names.

WHAT YOU HAVE LEARNED

This is an important chapter because so many of the programs you write in the future will interact with files. Once you have learned a few basic principles, working with files is not difficult.

The main thing to remember about text files is that *they contain only ASCII character codes.* Whether a sequence of digits ends up as a number or a string in your program depends on the type of variable in the `INPUT` statement. It is even possible to write a number onto a file from a numeric variable and later read it from that file into a string variable. Sounds funny, doesn't it, but that's the way text files work.

Remember that this chapter deals only with text files. True BASIC supports four other file types: random files, record files, stream files, and binary or byte files. Text files are the only file type that can be displayed by a simple text editor such as the True BASIC editor.

Topic	**Page**
A mental image of a file	47
How to open a file for input or output	48
When to close a file and why	52
How to write information on a file	52
How to read information from a file	54
Reading a line of text with LINE INPUT	55
How data is stored in a file	56
An imaginary pointer finds end of file	57
Constructing a simple DO loop	57
Memory data files and DATA statements	58

Figure 5.2 *What you have learned in Chapter 5.*

Looping and Branching

In preceding chapters, you have used two types of loops. When a program contains a loop, you probably noticed how the flow of statement execution changed, it was no longer sequential from the beginning of the program to the end. In this chapter you will learn about branching, more about looping, and the effect of these structures on the flow of program control.

6.1 MAKING A DECISION IN A LOOP

You have already seen how a logical function can be used to control a `DO` loop that is reading information from a text file. Let's look next at how general logical expressions can be used to control a loop.

Logical Expressions and Operators

Logical expressions are constructed using two variables or one variable and a value, connected by a logical operator. Here are the common logical operator symbols and their meanings:

>	greater than
>=	greater than or equal to
<	less than
<=	less than or equal to
=	equal
<>	not equal

As with logical functions, logical expressions can only have a value of true or false. For example, if the numeric variable `Power` has a value of 7, what is the value of the following expression?

```
Power > 5
```

If you said true, congratulations! If you said false, remember that the value of `Power` is 7 and 7 is greater than 5. Now try your hand at determining the values of the following logical expressions:

```
Power = 5
Power < 7
Power <= 7
Power > 7
```

Your answers should be false, false, true, and false.

Logical expressions are used most often with numeric variables and values, but they can also be used with string variables and values. The most commonly used operators with strings are "=" and "<>." For example, if `First$` has a value of "on" and `Last$` has a value of "on", then the expression

```
First$ = Last$
```

has a value of true. On the other hand, if `Last$` has a value of "On", the values of the two variables are not equal and the expression is false. To be equal, two strings must agree not only in the value, order, and number of specific characters but also in the case (upper or lower) of each character.

Try some experimentation yourself, writing short programs that display the values of logical expressions. Model your programs on the following example:

```
REM Example Program 6-1
REM Test a logical expression.

Power = 7
IF (Power > 5) then PRINT "true" else PRINT "false"
END
```

The second statement is called a single-line `IF` statement, one form of a branching statement. It almost reads like an English sentence—I will discuss it and other `IF` structures later in the chapter. In the meantime, I want to use it to display the value of a logical expression, true or false. The logical expression is enclosed in parentheses to make it more visible but these parentheses are not required.

As you know, the value of the logical expression (`Power > 5`) is true because 7 is greater than 5. In that case, the first `PRINT` statement displays a value of true. On the other hand, if the logical expression is false, the second `PRINT` statement displays a value of false.

A common error by beginning programmers is to write a statement that is correct English grammar and makes sense to them, but has incorrect True BASIC syntax. For example, the compound logical expression

```
Bridge > 23 or Bridge < 1
```

is correct syntax and true if a bridge number is outside the allowed range of 1 to 23. The equivalent English language expression

```
Bridge > 23 or < 1
```

may be perfectly understandable to you but True BASIC does not understand it. The statement syntax does not follow True BASIC's rules. You must be careful to write computer statements with the proper syntax because statements with incorrect syntax are rejected by the editor.

Challenge Problem 6-1

Write a program that displays 5 logical expressions and their values. The values should be "`true`" for true or "`false`" for false. Use the preceding program as a guide. An example logical expression and its value should be displayed in the following format:

```
(7 < 5) has a value of false
```

If you feel ambitious, try a compound logical expression that consists of two simple logical expressions joined together by a conjunction, `AND` or `OR`. A compound expression with `AND` is true only if both the simple expressions are true. A compound expression with `OR` is true if either of the simple expressions is true or if both are true. Here is another example:

```
(1 = 2) or (7 > 5) has a value of true
```

This compound expression is true because the expression (7 > 5) is true. See your manual for information on other conjunctions.

The DO Loop Again

You saw in Chapter 5 how a logical function is used to control a `DO` loop. Now look at how a logical expression can be used for the same purpose. The following program writes information on a text file, stopping when a single period is entered as the only character in a line:

```
! Example Program 6-2
! Write a text file, stopping when
! a single period is entered.

OPEN #1: name "A:\EX6-1.DAT", create newold
ERASE #1          !in case the file already exists
PRINT "Type a text line after each question mark";
PRINT "Enter a single period to stop."
DO
   LINE INPUT prompt "? ": Reply$
   PRINT #1, Reply$
LOOP until Reply$ = "."
CLOSE #1
PRINT "File EX6-1.DAT has been written."
END
```

Here is the output that might be displayed when Example Program 6-2 is executed:

```
Type a text line after each question mark.
Enter a single period to stop.
? This is the first line of entered text
? and this is the last line.
? .
File EX6-1.DAT has been written.
```

A prompt in the `LINE INPUT` statement displays a question mark when the program is ready for input. Unlike the `INPUT` statement, the `LINE INPUT` statement does not display a question mark automatically.

In this example, the test for whether or not to stop the program occurs in the `LOOP` statement at the end of the loop. This test can be either at the beginning of the loop — as part of the `DO` statement — or at the end of the loop. In the present case, it makes more sense to put it at the end because by that time the user has entered input that can be tested.

In addition to the `UNTIL` test, you have the option of using a `WHILE` test. The logic of these two tests is reversed — if one is true, the other is false. Here is a program fragment that shows how just the loop is changed:

```
DO
   LINE INPUT prompt "? ": Reply$
   PRINT #1, Reply$
LOOP while Reply$ <> "."
```

Notice that this test says to continue looping while the value of `Reply$` is not a single period. In this program, it creates logic that probably is harder to understand and is less clear than the original program. In other programs, however, the `WHILE` test may be more suitable than the `UNTIL` test.

Improving a Program Step by Step

You haven't yet examined the file EX6-1.DAT which contains the following data:

```
This is the first line of entered text
and this is the last line.
```

That final period may bother you as it does me. After all, you entered the final period only as a signal to the computer to stop prompting for input and to close the file. It shouldn't be in the file. How can you get rid of it?

Situations like this arise often in program development, so let's look at this case in some detail. I have two points to make. First, after writing the first draft of a program, you often see room for improvement and you should proceed to rewrite the program. I see nothing wrong with that process — it is very natural. After all, most books and manuals are written in a similar manner, first a draft and then one or more edits.

Second, before making changes in the program code to solve any problem, stop and think. The worst thing you can do is to rush in and start making lots of little changes at random. Think carefully before you act!

Just what is the problem?	*Well, an extra period got into the file.*
How did it get there?	*A* `PRINT` *statement was executed after the period was entered but before the test.*
Think through the process step-by-step:	*I am thinking, thinking hard.*
What do you expect the user to do first?	*Enter a line of text or a period.*
What do you do if it is a line of text?	*Write it on the file.*
What do you do if it is a period?	*Stop the loop without writing the period.*

You might develop the following outline, either in your head or on paper:

- Ask for the first item of input
- Start a loop
- Test the item, if it is a period, exit the loop
- If it is not a period, write it on the file
- Ask for the next item of input
- Go back to the start of the loop

After a while, you can develop this kind of outline in your mind but while learning to write programs, I recommend that you write the outline down in detail. Stop now, study the outline, and rewrite Example Program 6-2 on paper or on your computer. Don't look at the next example program until you have tried to write the program yourself — you'll learn more that way.

Here is a modified version of the preceding program. Remember, there is nothing wrong with having more than one `INPUT` statement in a program, maybe one within a loop and one outside the loop.

```
! Example Program 6-3
! Write a text file, stopping
! when a single period is entered.

OPEN #1: name "A:\EX6-1.DAT", create newold
ERASE #1           !in case the file already exists
PRINT "Type a text line after each question mark."
PRINT "Enter a single period to stop."
LINE INPUT prompt "? ": Reply$          !first input
DO until Reply$ = "."
   PRINT #1: Reply$
   LINE INPUT prompt "? ": Reply$       !next input
LOOP
CLOSE #1
PRINT "File EX6-1.DAT has been written."
END
```

Verify for yourself that user interaction is unchanged from Example Program 6-2 and that file EX5-1.DAT does not contain a line with a single period. This is a better program, isn't it?

6.2 DECISION MAKING: The IF Branch

So far, most of the example programs make a decision or test the value of a variable at the beginning or end of a loop. Now let's look at other decision-making structures.

Two-Way Branching

True BASIC has a general branching structure that allows a two-way decision to be made almost anywhere, taking one action if a logical expression (abbreviated here as `LE`) is true and another action if `LE` is false. Here is the structure:

```
IF <LE> then
   <execute this block if LE is true>
   <and go to the END IF statement>
ELSE
   <execute this block if LE is false>
END IF
```

This structure is very similar to the first, single-line branching statement in the chapter, it differs by having a multiline structure and adding a required `END IF` statement as the last line of the structure. The comments in angle brackets would normally be replaced by program statements. The `ELSE` statement and the block of statements after it is optional, as you will see in one of the following examples:

```
! Example Program 6-4
! Using a two-branch IF structure.

LET WidthOfOpening = 61.5  !inches
INPUT prompt "Width in inches? ": WidthOfItem

IF WidthOfItem < WidthOfOpening then
   PRINT "No problem installing the engine."
ELSE
   PRINT "Disassemble before installing."
END IF
END
```

Typical output might be as follows:

```
Width in inches? 60
No problem installing the engine.
```

This program might be part of a more complex program used by engineers to determine if a particular engine assembly can be used as a replacement for an existing engine. You can easily imagine the advantages of running this program before trying to install a new engine — and suddenly finding that it won't fit!

TIP: A common mistake made by beginning programmers is to leave off the required `END IF` statement. Note that `END IF` must be two separate words.

A Simple IF Statement

The next example program demonstrates the one-branch `IF` structure. In spite of its name, this structure still has two outcomes, either a message is printed or is not printed.

```
! Example Program 6-5
! Using a one-branch IF structure.

LET WidthOfOpening = 61.5  !inches
INPUT prompt "Width in inches? ": WidthOfItem

IF WidthOfItem >= WidthOfOpening then
   PRINT "Disassemble before installing."
END IF
END
```

This program displays a message only if the engine is too wide for installation, as shown:

```
Width in inches? 63
Disassemble before installing.
```

Multiple Branching

The last example program of this set shows the multibranch IF structure. For three branches, two logical expressions must be tested. It is possible, of course, to have as many branches as you want and to include more than one statement in a branch.

```
! Example Program 6-6
! Using a multibranch IF structure.

LET WidthOfOpening = 61.5  !inches
INPUT PROMPT "Width in inches? ": WidthOfItem

IF WidthOfItem > WidthOfOpening then
   PRINT "Disassemble before installing."
ELSEIF WidthOfItem = WidthOfOpening then
   PRINT "Engine may fit with no problem"
   PRINT "but we recommend disassembly."
ELSE
   PRINT "No problem installing the engine."
END IF
END
```

The output from this program might look as follows:

```
Width in inches? 61.5
Engine may fit with no problem
but we recommend disassembly.
```

So there you have the story of the IF structure and its branches and its ability to make decisions. This structure adds great power to a computer program.

Challenge Problem 6-2

Now that you know how computer programs can make decisions, go back and look at Challenge Problem 3-2. How can you create a solution to this problem that does not require user input? Hint: What must be the values of the Row and Column indices for an element containing the value 1. Write a new program without user input for this problem.

6.3 The SELECT CASE Structure

Another multibranch structure in True BASIC is the SELECT CASE structure — often preferable when more than two branches are required. Here is the structure:

```
SELECT CASE test expression
CASE test1, test2
     first block of statements
CASE test3
     second block of statements
```

```
CASE test4, test5, test6
     third block of statements
CASE ELSE
     fourth block of statements
END SELECT
```

The "test expression" in the first line may be any expression or variable, string or numeric. If any test is satisfied, the block of statements associated with that test is executed and control jumps to the statement after `END SELECT`. If no test is satisfied, the fourth block of statements after `CASE ELSE` is executed. `CASE ELSE` and its associated block of statements are optional but usually recommended.

Assume the test expression in a `SELECT CASE` statement is the numeric variable `Choice`. A `CASE` statement with two equality tests might be

```
CASE 7, -5
```

and is satisfied if `Choice` has a value of 7 or -5, as shown in the following program fragment:

```
SELECT CASE Choice
CASE 7, -5
     PRINT "Choice has a value of 7 or -5."
END SELECT
```

A `CASE` statement with a range test might be

```
CASE 14 to 21
```

and is satisfied if `Choice` has a value between 14 and 21 inclusive. The program fragment then looks as follows:

```
SELECT CASE Choice
CASE 7, -5
     PRINT "Choice has a value of 7 or -5."
CASE 14 to 21
     PRINT "Choice has a value from 14 through 21."
END SELECT
```

A `CASE` statement with a logical comparison, in the form "is op value", might be

```
CASE is > 175
```

and is satisfied if `Choice` has a value greater than 175. The symbol "op" means one of the logical operators. The program fragment then looks as follows:

```
SELECT CASE Choice
CASE 7, -5
     PRINT "Choice has a value of 7 or -5."
CASE 14 to 21
     PRINT "Choice has a value from 14 through 21."
```

```
CASE is > 175
     PRINT "Choice has a value greater than 175."
END SELECT
```

Note that only constants can be used in a CASE test, variables or expressions are not allowed.

Here is another example program that uses a string variable as a test expression in a SELECT CASE structure. This program might be part of a larger program.

```
! Example Program 6-7
! Interpret the answer to a question.

INPUT prompt "Your answer? ": Ans$
SELECT CASE Ans$

CASE "Y", "y"
     PRINT "The answer is YES. "

CASE "N", "n"
     PRINT "The answer is NO."

CASE else
     PRINT "Please answer Y or N."

END SELECT
END
```

Two examples of program output are shown:

```
Your answer? n
The answer is NO.

Your answer? q
Please answer Y or N.
```

6.4 FORMATTING OF SCREEN DISPLAYS

You can exercise some control over the format of screen displays by using commas or semicolons as separators in PRINT statements and by using a trailing semicolon. There are times, however, when you need greater control, especially when displaying numbers. The PRINT USING statement fulfills that need.

The general syntax of this statement is as follows:

```
PRINT using Format$: Item1, Item2,...
```

The quantity Format$ can be either a string value or a string variable, containing ordinary characters as well as special characters called *format characters*. Any characters that are not format characters are just displayed on the screen.

Commas in the list of items have no influence on format, they are used only as separators. The trailing semicolon, however, can still be used to suppress the normal line feed and carriage return at the end of a line.

Before going further, I need to identify all the format characters. You probably will use only a few of them but you need access to a complete list so you won't try to use a format character as an ordinary display character.

Here are the numeric format characters:

#	any digit, display leading zeroes as spaces
%	any digit, display leading zeroes as zeroes
*	any digit, display leading zeroes as asterisks
+	display number with leading plus or minus sign
-	display number with leading space or minus sign
$	display number with a leading dollar sign
^	display the exponential field of a number

The string format characters are as follows:

#	any ordinary character (not a format character)
<	any ordinary character in a left-justified string
>	any ordinary character in a right-justified string

While I discuss only a few of the numeric format characters, information on all format characters is available in your manual.

Displaying Simple Numbers

The most common format character (#) is used to represent any digit in a displayed number. Remember that a format string just changes the appearance of a displayed number, the actual value of the number is not changed. Here is an example program that illustrates its use:

```
! Example Program 6-8
! Use PRINT USING to display several numbers.

PRINT using "####": 125
PRINT using "####": 1285.9
```

```
PRINT using "####": 12500
PRINT
PRINT using "###.##": 12.5
PRINT using "###.##": -12.521
PRINT using "###.##": -125.21
PRINT
PRINT using "###,###.##": 35305
END
```

The following results are displayed

```
 125
1286
****

 12.50
-12.52
******

 35,305.00
```

The results are a little surprising, aren't they? Let me explain them. In the first place, the lines of asterisks indicate errors, the number could not be displayed properly in the space provided by the format string. The number 12500 is too long to fit into a 4-digit space. The negative number -125.21 has too many characters (including the minus sign) to fit into the 3-digit space before the decimal point. You must be careful when writing format strings; if they are too short, the displayed asterisks ruin an otherwise-well-formatted report.

Look at the other results. Numbers are right-justified if the format string is longer than needed. Trailing zeroes are added to a decimal number or the number is rounded off, matching the number of format characters after the decimal point. The last example shows how to insert a comma into a displayed number.

The format string can be a string variable instead of a string value, a numeric variable can be formatted instead of a numeric value. Note this program fragment:

```
LET Number = 125
LET Format$ = "####"
PRINT using Format$: Number
```

Finally, ordinary characters can be combined with format characters to display a number with labels, as shown:

```
PRINT using "The distance is ### miles.": 235.7
```

This statement produces the following display:

```
The distance is 236 miles.
```

Displaying Numbers as Dollar Amounts

Another common use of `PRINT USING` is to display currency amounts, using the dollar sign ($) as a format character. Usually, you want a dollar sign to "float" with the size of the number, appearing just before the first digit. The following type of statement produces that result:

```
PRINT using "$$$$$$.##": Amount
```

All dollar signs except the leftmost dollar sign serve as format characters, the leftmost dollar sign is displayed as a floating dollar sign. There is no space between the dollar sign and the displayed digits. The following example program explains, probably better than words, how this all works:

```
! Example Program 6-9
! Display formatted dollar amounts.

DO while more data
   READ Cost
   PRINT using "$$$$$$.##": Cost
LOOP

DATA 23.75, 1244, 0.237, 12345.6, 123456.7
END
```

Here is the formatted output:

```
   $23.75
 $1244.00
     $.24
$12345.60
*********
```

Notice that decimal digits — digits after the decimal point — are rounded to two digits, that a dollar sign floats just to the left of the leftmost digit, and that the number can have no more than five digits preceding the decimal point. The number $.24 looks kind of strange, doesn't it? I would avoid this format for amounts less than $1.00.

True BASIC does not accept a comma in a format string of dollar signs, as it accepted a comma in the last format string of Example Program 6-8. There is no easy way in True BASIC to display a dollar amount in the common form: $12,500.00. You must first convert the number to a string and then add the other characters you need. See the discussion in Appendix D.

6.5 BRIDGE INSPECTION, PART II

I finished Chapter 3 with the uncomfortable feeling that while I may have convinced you of the utility of the array structure, I had not convinced you of its practicality. Remember the bridge inspection problem where 5 teams measured the natural frequencies of 23 bridges? You may have imagined each team writing its measured results down in notebooks or on a little slips of paper. You probably wondered how the 115 separate frequency measurements are entered into an array, and how many slips are misplaced or incorrect measurements entered. You may also have wondered why these frequencies are placed in an array in the first place.

Let me answer these questions and explain how the data might be handled. Little slips of paper are out, computers are in! Assume that each team has a laptop computer and all measurement information is written on disk in that computer, using an application program designed for that purpose. Each time a team enters a measurement, the team's number, the bridge's number, and the frequency value must be specified. It may be that some of this data entry process is automated — if a team always uses the same laptop, its number can be entered automatically. Assume the recording program is designed to detect incorrect entries, to allow a team to correct errors in measurement, to back up every piece of information, and so forth. Stop for a moment and think about any other conditions you might want to specify if you were writing the data-gathering program.

At the end of every day, the information on each laptop is loaded down to a central computer. A text file is created containing lines of information. Each line contains a team's number, a bridge number, and a natural frequency value. Assume these three numbers are separated from each other by commas. The line for team 2 measuring a natural frequency of 5.34 hertz on bridge 11 might look as follows:

```
2,11,5.34
```

Filling an Array from a Text File

Given this file of raw data, it is relatively easy to fill an array with score values. You probably remember that the array was named `BridgeRecord` and defined by the following statement:

```
DIM BridgeRecord(1 to 23, 1 to 5)
```

How can this array be used? There are many choices. For example, the average frequency for any bridge as measured by all five teams can be quickly calculated. The average frequency for all 23 bridges measured by each team might indicate that one team's instruments are out of calibration, or that the team's measurement techniques are different from those of the other teams. In general, when the frequency data is arranged in an array, various statistical and analytical methods can be easily applied.

To give you practice working with a reasonably large file, I have prepared a file containing the natural frequencies for all the bridges as measured by all teams. This file is named FREQS.DAT and is on the floppy disk included with this book. Here is an example program that reads the file and assigns its scores to an array:

```
! Example Program 6-10
! Read file data and assign it to an array.

OPEN #1: name "A:\FREQS.DAT", access input
DIM BridgeRecord(1 to 23, 1 to 5)
DO until End #1
   INPUT #1: Bridge, Team, Frequency
   LET BridgeRecord(Bridge, Team) = Frequency
LOOP
PRINT "File A:\FREQS.DAT has been read."
END
```

This program is deceptively simple considering the amount of work it does. It reads all information from the file and assigns all measurements to an array. You may be surprised to see one `INPUT` statement reading three items from the file — that's not what I recommended previously. However, because I knew that this file was originally written with commas separating the three numbers on each line, it is easier to read these numbers with one `INPUT` statement into three different variables. Just another case of the exception proving the rule. If the file had been written with only one number per line, then a different `INPUT` statement would be needed.

If you have trouble understanding this concept, write a little experimental program that reads data from file FREQS.DAT into a single numeric variable, one line at a time. What happens? Be sure you understand thoroughly the mechanics of reading data from a text file.

Displaying Data from an Array

Now you can use the preceding example program as part of a larger program that displays the frequency measurements for any bridge. I have added lots of remarks in bold face to help you follow the program logic.

```
! Example Program 6-11
! Read file data and assign data to an array.

OPEN #1: name "A:\FREQS.DAT", access input

DIM BridgeRecord(1:23, 1:5)                        !Define array
DO until End #1                        !Until end of file, read data
   INPUT #1: Bridge, Team, Frequency               !from file and
   LET BridgeRecord(Bridge, Team) = Frequency      !assign
LOOP                                               !to the array
```

```
! Ask user to enter a bridge number and
! display the natural frequency of that bridge.

CLEAR                                       !Clear the output screen
PRINT "Enter zero to stop the program."
INPUT prompt "Bridge number? ": Bridge !Get number
DO until Bridge = 0                         !If not zero,
   PRINT "TEAM:        ";                   !display a label
   FOR Team = 1 to 5                        !and all the
     PRINT using " #   ": Team;             !team
   NEXT Team                                !numbers
   PRINT "Average"                          !Start a new line
   PRINT "FREQUENCY:  ";                    !Display a label
   LET Sum = 0                            !and initialize variable Sum
   FOR Team = 1 TO 5                        !For all teams,
      LET Freq = BridgeRecord(Bridge, Team)     !get the
      PRINT using "#.#  ": Freq;            !frequency and display
      LET Sum = Sum + Freq                  !Add frequency to Sum
   NEXT Team
   LET Average = Sum/5                      !Display the average
   PRINT using " #.##": Average             !natural frequency
   PRINT
   INPUT prompt "Bridge number? ": Bridge       !Get next
LOOP                                            !bridge number
END
```

Typical output looks as follows:

```
Enter zero to stop the program.
Bridge number? 6
TEAM:          1    2    3    4    5   Average
FREQUENCY:   5.2  5.1  5.3  5.1  5.0    5.14

Bridge number? 0
```

The `CLEAR` statement is new, it just clears the output screen before displaying the output of the current program. The large `DO` loop allows a user to continue entering bridge numbers as long as desired, with the entry of zero being a sign that the user wishes to stop the program. This use of a special entry — zero in this case — is sometimes called *using a sentinel* and is often seen in computer programs. Note that the sentinel (zero) cannot be a valid bridge number.

You may wonder why I assigned the value of an array element to the variable `Freq` (for frequency) and then used `Freq` in the next two statements. The real reason is that otherwise I would have had a statement too long to fit on the page and I didn't want to extend the statement over two lines. It is also true, however, that the program as written may execute a little more quickly because the array `BridgeRecord` is accessed only once within the loop body.

I have already discussed formatting of output but this program is more complicated than previous ones. A combination of trailing semicolons and `PRINT USING` statements is used. Don't think that I wrote this program correctly from scratch. I first wrote a draft version, saw ways to improve the formatting and did so, and finally got results that satisfied me. I recommend you follow that method when writing your own programs.

A last program in this series uses an array to analyze measurements taken by the 5 teams. I suggest a simple method of analysis, averaging each teams results for the 23 bridges. Here is a slightly modified version of Example Program 6-11:

```
! Example Program 6-12
! Read data file and assign data to an array.

OPEN #1: name "A:\FREQS.DAT", access input
!Open the file FREQS.DAT for reading

DIM BridgeRecord(1:23, 1:5)          !Define array
DO until End #1                      !Until end of file, read data
   INPUT #1: Bridge, Team, Frequency           !from file and
   LET BridgeRecord(Bridge, Team) = Frequency  !assign
LOOP                                           !to array

! Calculate the average frequency
! measured by each of the teams.

CLEAR                            !Clear the output screen
PRINT "Average of each team's frequency"
PRINT "measurements for all bridges:"
PRINT
PRINT "TEAM:  ";                               !Display a label
FOR Team = 1 TO 5                              !and all the
   PRINT using " #   ": Team;                  !bridge
NEXT Team                                      !numbers
PRINT                                !Start a new line of output
PRINT "FREQ:  ";                     !Display a label
FOR Team = 1 TO 5                    !For each team,
   LET Sum = 0                       !initialize Sum to zero and
   FOR Bridge = 1 to 23              !add up the frequency
      LET Freq = BridgeRecord(Bridge, Team)!measurements
      LET Sum = Sum + Freq                     !of all
   NEXT Bridge                                 !the bridges
   LET AverageFrequency = Sum / 23             !Calculate and
   PRINT using "#.## ": AverageFrequency;      !display the
NEXT Team                            !average frequency
END                                  !of all bridges
```

The following output is produced:

```
Average of each team's frequency
measurements for all bridges:

TEAM:    1    2    3    4    5
FREQ:  5.43 5.44 5.56 5.43 5.44
```

A new variable `Sum` is used to hold the sum of all frequencies for each team and then the average frequency measured by that team is calculated. These results are not assigned to an array because they are used only once for display. They could, however, be placed in an array if you plan to use them again in the program. Note that `Sum` is initialized to zero before calculating a new sum and average frequency.

Looking at the example output, the results appear to be remarkably consistent except for team 3. If I was the engineer in charge of this project and saw these results, I would immediately calibrate the instruments used by team 3. Just looking at the results from the previous example problem, however, I am not sure I would notice that these instruments appear to be reading high.

Challenge Problem 6-3

Engineers often have to prepare reports containing cost estimates. Assume you have written a program that assigns the cost of labor to a variable named `Labor` and the cost of materials to a variable named `Materials`. The total cost is assigned to a variable named `Total`. Write a program that displays the values of these variables in the format and using the amounts shown:

```
Labor            $12500.50
Materials         $7030.83
                -----------
Total            $19531.33
```

WHAT YOU HAVE LEARNED

With this chapter, I complete a discussion of the various control structures that give computer programs so much of their power. Branching and looping are important additions to the simple sequential execution of program statements. You also see the key role played by logical expressions with their logical operators and I hope you now understand why computer programmers must be able to think logically.

Finally, you go back to the bridge problem and see how to fill an array from a text file, as well as how to use an array for analysis and display.

Topic	Page
Logical operators in logical expressions	63
The UNTIL and WHILE tests in a DO loop	66
Improving the first draft of a program	66
Decision making and the IF statement	68
SELECT CASE structure	70
Formatting numbers displayed on the screen	72
Assigning values to an array from a text file	76
Analyzing data in an array	77

Figure 6.1*—What you have learned in Chapter 6.*

Built-In Functions

Functions are the icing on the program cake. There are over 100 built-in functions, most are listed and discussed in the FUNCTION.TRU help file. In this chapter, you learn about a dozen or so of the most-often-used functions.

7.1 DEFINITION OF A FUNCTION

A *function* is defined as a block of computer code that performs some calculation or manipulation, usually a calculation, and typically returns a value. The function can either be part of the language system (*built-in function*) or be written by the programmer (*programmed function*). In this chapter, I discuss only built-in functions, programmed functions are discussed in Chapter 8.

Every function has a *name* and if a calculation is made, the result of that calculation is assigned to the function's name. In computer terminology, a function is *called* when its name is used as part of an expression in a program known as the *calling program*. The value calculated by the function code is *returned* when that value is made available to the calling program. A function usually has *arguments*, one or more values, variables, or expressions that are *passed* or made available to the function when it is called.

TIP: There are lots of definitions in the preceding paragraphs but they are **all** important. You must learn them because they will be used frequently in this and following chapters.

An Example Function

Let's look at a function that you have used before:

```
! Example Program 7-1
! Using a built-in function.

LET Nmbr = 9
PRINT Sqr(Nmbr)
END
```

A value of 3 is displayed. As you know, 3 is the square root of 9. Example Program 7-1 is the calling program, `Sqr` is the name of the function, and `Nmbr` is its single argument.

When the program is executed, the function `Sqr` is called, the value of `Nmbr` is passed to it, a value of 3 is calculated in the function code itself and assigned to the function name `Sqr`, and this assigned value of `Sqr` is returned to the calling program and displayed. Be sure you understand the organization of a function and how it works — this is an important step in learning to write computer programs.

Other Definitions

There are two general classes of functions — *numeric functions* and *string functions*. Numeric functions return numeric values, their names cannot contain dollar signs. String functions return string values, their names must end with a dollar sign. There are also a few special functions like the logical function `End #`.

Remember that a numeric expression is defined as two or more numeric values, numeric variables, or numeric functions joined together by arithmetic operators. A sting expression can be created by concatenating – joining together – two or more string values, string variables, or string functions.

NOTE: The notation I use displays the function name followed by one or more symbolic names that indicate the argument types. The usual symbolic argument names are `Nmbr` for a number and `Strg$` for a string.

7.2 ARITHMETIC FUNCTIONS

You have already used the function `Round(Nmbr, N)`. Let's examine it and other arithmetic functions in greater detail.

Functions That Modify Numbers

These functions are used to modify numbers. As you know, the `Round` function controls the number of *decimal digits* — defined as digits located after the decimal point. Here are six examples:

`Round(100.39,0)`	returns a value of 100
`Round(100.39)`	also returns a value of 100
`Round(100.39,1)`	returns a value of 100.4
`Round(100.39,2)`	returns a value of 100.39
`Round(100.39,3)`	also returns a value of 100.39
`Round(-17.5)`	returns a value of -17
`Round(17.5)`	returns a value of 18

Be careful with negative numbers, the results can be surprising! The decimal value 0.5 is rounded up with a positive number but made less negative — you might still call it rounded up — with a negative number. Note in the fifth example that the `Round` function does not add a trailing zero after the decimal point, you must use the `PRINT USING` statement to display a number with trailing zeroes.

You should understand the difference between a function like `Round` and the `PRINT USING` statement. The function actually changes the value of its first argument — the first number in parentheses — while the `PRINT USING` statement only changes the way a number is displayed.

Look at the following test program, try to determine before you run the program what results will be displayed, and then run the program:

```
! Example Program 7-2
! A simple test of the Round function.

LET X = 12.86
PRINT X/2
PRINT Round(X,1)/2
END
```

Was the answer you expected the same as the answer displayed? The `Round` function changed the value of `X` to 12.9 so when it was divided by 2, the result displayed is 6.45. This simple test program is a good example of the experimentation I recommended in Chapter 2. By the way, here is the program output:

```
6.43
6.45
```

Another function similar to `Round` but slightly different is the `Int` function. I don't find it as useful but you should look it up in your manual or help file.

Sometimes you want to isolate that part of a number preceding or following the decimal point. The function `Ip(Nmbr)` returns the *integer part* of a number while the function `Fp(Nmbr)` returns the *fractional part*:

`Ip(12.97)`	returns a value of 12
`Fp(12.97)`	returns a value of .97
`Ip(-7.5)`	returns a value of -7
`Fp(-7.5)`	returns a value of -.5

As you might expect, both the integer and fractional parts of the value -7.5 are returned as negative values.

The `Abs(Nmbr)` function returns the absolute value of `Nmbr`. Two examples are shown:

`Abs(5)` returns a value of 5
`Abs(-5)` returns a value of 5

One common use of the `Abs` function is to change a negative number to a positive number by deleting the minus sign.

Mathematical Functions

Mathematical functions and formulas are of particular interest to engineers. Six arithmetic functions in this group are discussed. The trigonometric functions – `Sin`, `Cos`, and `Tan` – requires arguments in units of radians, not degrees. Beginning programmers often forget this requirement. Look at this example:

`Sin(Pi/4)` returns a value 0.707107

The angle Pi/4 radians is the same as the angle 45 degrees. If you don't want to use radian units, the conversion function `Rad(Angle)` converts an angle in degrees into radians. For example, the sine of 45 degrees is calculated by the following expression:

`Sin(Rad(45))` returns a value of 0.707107

True BASIC provides an alternative way to calculate trigonometric functions of angles that are expressed in degrees. If you include the statement

```
OPTION ANGLE degrees
```

near the beginning of your program (before the first executable statement), any trigonometric function expects an angle argument in units of degrees. The preceding statement can thus be written:

```
OPTION ANGLE degrees
Sin(45)
```

and produces the same result as before.

The logarithmic function (`Log`) returns the natural logarithm – logarithm to the base *e* – of its argument. If you want to calculate a logarithm to the base 10, use the function `Log10(Nmbr)`. For example,

```
Log10(1000) returns a value of 3
```

meaning that the base (10) raised to the power 3 equals 1000. Take advantage of True BASIC to refresh your memory of logarithms.

The arctangent function (`Atn`) returns a value in radians. You probably don't remember that the angle whose tangent is 1 is an angle of 0.7854 radians but you may remember that it is an angle of 45 degrees. Run this short program to check it out:

```
OPTION ANGLE degrees
PRINT Atn(1)
END
```

Did you get the correct answer?

The exponential function (`Exp`) is closely associated with the `Log` function. You may remember that

`Log(Exp(7))` returns a value of 7

because the two functions are reciprocals. What is the value of `Exp(Log(7))`? Use True BASIC to find out.

The FUNCTION.TRU help file provides additional information on all functions including mathematical functions.

Challenge Problem 7-1

Write a program to calculate the volume of a balloon that is 35 feet in diameter. Assume the balloon is a sphere. The volume of a sphere is given by the following formula:

```
Volume = (4 * Pi * (Radius ^ 3)) / 3
```

Calculate your answer in cubic feet and display with two decimal digits.

As an extra challenge, try writing a short program to calculate the area of a triangle given the lengths of two sides and the included angle between those two sides. If you don't know the formula, look it up.

7.3 CONVERSION FUNCTIONS

Let's look next at two pairs of conversion functions that provide additional flexibility in writing programs.

ASCII Conversions

Every character and symbol that can appear in a True BASIC string has an ASCII code value. There are 256 characters, some of them printing characters and some non-printing. The first 128 ASCII values – called the standard ASCII set – are listed in Appendix F.

The `Ord(Strg$)` function returns the ASCII value of the character in its string argument. Only one character is allowed, as shown:

`Ord("\")`	returns a value of 92
`Ord("A")`	returns a value of 65
`Ord("ABC")`	returns an error message, "Improper Ord string"

The `Chr$(Nmbr)` function is a complement of the preceding function, it returns the character or symbol corresponding to the ASCII code value of its argument. The argument `Nmbr` must be between 0 and 255, inclusive. Here are two examples:

`Chr$(65)`	returns a value of "A"
`Chr$(124)`	returns a vertical line symbol

Conversions Between Numbers and Strings

If a string of digits is read from a file, it is often necessary to convert that string to a number using the `Val(Strg$)` function. The string must have the format of a valid number; for example, it may include a decimal point and a plus or minus sign as well as digits. Some examples follow:

`Val("-17.7")`	returns the number -17.7
`Val("+17.0")`	returns the number 17

Also consider these two additional examples that are invalid:

`Val("abc")`	returns the following error message, "Val string isn't a proper number"
`Val("12,500")`	returns the same error message

The complementary function **`Str$(Nmbr)`** requires that **`Nmbr`** be a valid number. The second of the following pair of examples does not contain a valid number:

`Str$(-17.7)`	returns the string "-17.7"
`Str$(12,500)`	returns an error message

NOTE: True BASIC considers the second example in each of the preceding two cases to be an error because commas are not allowed in numbers.

For more information on the display of numbers, especially numbers in exponential or scientific notation, read Appendix D.

7.4 STRING FUNCTIONS

You are introduced next to a group of functions that are very important when working with text. These functions either return a modified string or return information about the string. Let's look first at three functions that return information.

Returning String Information

The first function, named `Pos`, provides a powerful method for analyzing a string. It searches for the position of one or more characters in a string. Here is its syntax:

```
Pos(Target$, Pattern$, N)
```

There are two string arguments. The argument `Target$` is the string that is searched. The computer looks in `Target$` for the pattern contained in argument `Pattern$`.

TIP: In many practical applications, the string `Pattern$` is only a single character.

If the argument `N` is omitted, searching starts at the first character of `Target$`, otherwise searching starts at the `N`th character. Searching is from left to right and character position is measured from the left end of the string; the first character is in position 1, the second in position 2, and so forth.

This function returns the position of the string `Pattern$` in `Target$`; that is, the position of the first character in `Target$` where a match occurs. I know this explanation is complicated but some examples may help you understand better:

`Pos("ABCABC", "A")` returns the number 1

In the preceding example, an "A" is found in the first character position of "ABCABC."

`Pos("ABCABC", "AB", 2)` returns the number 4

In this example, searching starts at character position 2, the first "B" character. The first "AB" found after that position starts with the "A" in character position 4.

`Pos("green box", " ")` returns the number 6

In the last example, the function looks for the first space character and finds it in character position 6.

NOTE: Check your True BASIC reference manual or the FUNCTION.TRU help file for other variations of the `Pos` function.

There are times when it is more convenient to search a string from right to left, a task accomplished by the `Posr` function – a reverse position function. Searching now proceeds from right to left but character position is still measured from the left end of the `Target$` string. Maybe the following examples will help make that clear:

`Posr("abcde","d")`	returns the number 4
`Posr("abcde","b")`	returns the number 2
`Posr("abcab","b")`	returns the number 5
`Posr("abcab","b",4)`	returns the number 2

Be sure you understand that last example, it's a little tricky! Get help if you need it from a help file or the reference manual.

Another important property of a string is its length in characters, returned by the `Len` function. Here is a simple example:

`Len("red fox")` returns the number 7

Remember that a space is a perfectly valid character and is counted as such.

Creating Substrings

True BASIC allows you to access substrings, defined as sequences of contiguous characters within string variables. An expression in square brackets, `[a:b]`, following a string variable name, designates a substring that starts at the character in position "a" and ends at the character in position "b." The positions "a" and "b" are numbers representing character positions where as before, the leftmost character in a string is in character position 1. Here is a program fragment that displays two substrings:

```
LET Name$ = "lunar orbit"
PRINT Name$[1:5]
PRINT Name$[7:11]
```

The following output is displayed:

```
lunar
orbit
```

In this example, it is easy to extract the two words contained in `Name$` because the position of the space separating the words is known.

In many cases, however, the contents of the target string are not known. The function `Pos` and this substring capability can be used together, first to find the location of the separator character (often a space) and then to extract the two substrings of interest. The next example program shows how to separate a user-entered name into a first name and a last name:

```
! Example Program 7-3
! Extract first and last names.

LINE INPUT prompt "Enter your name: ": Name$
PRINT
LET LastChar = Len(Name$)
LET Space = Pos(Name$, " ")
```

```
LET FirstName$ = Name$[1:(Space - 1)]
PRINT "First name: "; FirstName$
LET LastName$ = Name$[(Space + 1):LastChar]
PRINT "Last name: "; LastName$
END
```

This program works fine as long as the user enters a name consisting only of a first name and a last name, as shown:

```
Enter your name: Mary White

First name: Mary
Last name: White
```

Study Example Program 7-3 carefully and run it several times. Be sure you understand exactly how it works. This type of analysis is commonly used in many programs that manipulate text. In fact, most string manipulation in True BASIC programs requires the use of one or more string functions and the substring capability.

TIP: Instead of calculating the position of the last character in the name string and assigning that position to `LastChar`, you can use any large number – larger that the length of the string – as the second argument of `LastName$`. I often use the large number `Maxnum` for this purpose, as shown:

```
LET LastName$ = Name$[(Space + 1):Maxnum]
```

The analysis used in this program breaks down, however, if the user enters names like Mary J. White or A. Brandis Jones. Try entering these names yourself. What happens? How can the program be improved? One way is to look for all the spaces, then extract the first, middle, and last names or initials.

Challenge Problem 7-2

Write a program to extract the first and last names from a name that includes a middle initial. Extra challenge: Modify your program so it will also work for names that have no middle initial. Extra extra challenge: Modify your program so it will also work with names like A. Brandis Jones or Mary J. B. White.

Changing Case

The `Lcase$(Strg$)` function changes all alphabetic characters in the argument `Strg$` to lowercase. `Ucase$(Strg$)` does just the opposite, changing all alphabetic characters to uppercase. Only alphabetic characters are changed. Here are two examples

`Ucase$("Key")` returns the string “KEY”
`Lcase$("Key")` returns the string “key”

These functions are especially useful when comparing two strings for equality, as in sorting and searching operations. Remember that True BASIC considers two strings equal only if they agree in their sequence of characters and in the case — upper or lower — of each character. Thus the strings Key, KEY, and key are all considered different strings by True BASIC.

On the other hand, most people consider these three versions of Key as the same or equal. To make a program behave as you or I would expect, you can change the two strings being compared to the same case before making the comparison, using either the `Ucase$` or `Lcase$` function. Look at the following example:

```
! Example Program 7-4
! Compare two entered names.

PRINT "Enter the first name: ";
LINE INPUT FirstName$
PRINT "Enter the second name: ";
LINE INPUT SecondName$
PRINT
IF Ucase$(FirstName$) = Ucase$(SecondName$) then
     PRINT "The two names are the same."
ELSE
     PRINT "The two names are different."
END IF
END
```

Here is an example of program output:

```
Enter the first name: Key
Enter the second name: key

The two names are the same.
```

7.5 COMPUTER SIMULATION FUNCTIONS

Computers are often used to simulate events or processes. A simple example is the roll of a pair of dice. More practical examples are the movements of an airplane wing in turbulent conditions, or the earnings of a new technology company under certain assumed economic conditions.

TIP: Almost every kind of simulation depends on random numbers generated by a random number generator.

Many simulations use random numbers created by a block of code called a *random number generator*. It takes a mathematician to define random numbers accurately and in detail. For our purposes, let's agree that a random number is a number generated by chance, and that there is no way to predict what the next number in a series of random numbers will be.

The Rnd function in True BASIC returns a random number that is greater than or equal to zero and less than one. Let's see what happens when Rnd is used to generate a sequence of four random numbers:

```
! Example Program 7-5
! Display a sequence of random numbers.

FOR Count = 1 TO 4
     PRINT Rnd;
 NEXT Count
PRINT
END
```

When I ran this program on my computer, it produced the following output:

```
 .7055475  .5334242  .5795186  .2895625
```

That looks like a pretty good set of random numbers, doesn't it? The results on your computer may be different but should be similar.

NOTE: The numbers returned by Rnd are properly called pseudorandom numbers. Again, only a mathematician would know the difference. These numbers are perfectly acceptable, however, for any kind of computer simulation program that I have ever seen.

Now run the program again and look at the output. Surprised? I was the first time — you get exactly the same sequence. The numbers in the sequence are indeed random, but each sequence is identical to the preceding sequence. What is happening is that the random number generator is starting at the same point each time the program is run. As they say in the mathematical world, its *seed value* remains the same.

One way to change the seed value is to include a RANDOMIZE statement near the beginning of your program before the code that contains function Rnd. This statement should appear only once within a program and not in a loop. Executing the statement more than once tends to make the results of Rnd less random and thus the program less accurate. The RANDOMIZE statement should be added to Example Program 7-5 so it can execute before the Rnd function executes, as shown in the following program fragment:

```
RANDOMIZE
FOR Count = 1 TO 4
     PRINT Rnd;
NEXT Count
```

Try running the modified program several times and examine the results.

Is there ever a situation when you don't want to use the RANDOMIZE statement? One situation may arise if you are trying to develop a new program using random numbers. By temporarily deleting the RANDOMIZE statement, you get the same random number sequence each time the program is run. That may make it easier to find errors. Try it yourself the next time you write a new program that uses the Rnd function.

Random Bridge Frequencies

Remember the bridge inspection programs and the file of natural frequencies? Here is how I generated the values in that file. I wanted to have five frequencies for each bridge, clustered within a limited range above a base frequency. I decided arbitrarily that the random base frequency should be between 2 hertz and 8 hertz, and that a random increment of 0 to 0.8 hertz should be added for each inspection team. This combination produces a range of frequencies from 2 to 8.8 with the five measurements for each bridge varying by no more than 0.8 hertz.

In this case, it doesn't matter what seed is used for Rnd because I am only going to run the program once to create a file. You might be interested, however, in what effect changing the seed has on the final scores. If so, add a RANDOMIZE statement.

Here is an example program, similar to but slightly different from the one I wrote, that generates frequencies and displays them on the screen (in an appropriate screen format) rather than writing them on a file:

```
! Example Program 7-6
! Create a list of bridge frequencies.

! Add RANDOMIZE here if wanted.
FOR Bridge = 1 TO 23
  LET BaseValue = 20 + Round(60 * Rnd)
  FOR Team = 1 TO 5
    LET BridgeValue = BaseValue + Round(8 * Rnd)
    LET Frequency = BridgeValue / 10
    PRINT using "#.#  ": Frequency;
  NEXT Team
  PRINT
NEXT Bridge
END
```

Note how random numbers are created with a range different than the default range of Rnd. The BaseValue expression 20 + Round(60 * Rnd) returns a random integer (whole number) between 0 and 80, inclusive. When Rnd returns its least value (0), the expression returns a value of 20. When Rnd returns its greatest value (0.9999...), the expression returns a value of 80. In a similar manner, the expression Round(8 * Rnd) returns a random integer between 0 and 8, inclusive. BridgeValue contains a random integer between 20 and 88, it is divided by 10 to create the value of Frequency. Here are a few lines of program output:

```
4.6  4.3  4.1  4.4  4.3
7.5  8.0  8.0  7.9  7.6
7.8  7.8  7.9  7.7  8.0
5.3  5.1  5.7  5.2  5.0
```

Remember that this output is formatted for display. A somewhat different format is used for writing scores on a file. One other point: The distribution of scores is not uniform over the full range from 2 to 8.8, there are fewer scores at the beginning and end of that range. Creating a uniform distribution is more difficult and in this case, not really necessary.

Challenge Problem 7-3

Write a program that simulates the roll of a pair of dice. Display two numbers representing the value of each die (that is the singular of dice). Design your program for multiple rolls, maybe having it make the number of rolls specified by the user or continue rolling the dice until some signal is entered by the user.

WHAT YOU HAVE LEARNED

I have introduced you to only a few of True BASIC's built-in functions. To help you find out what other functions are available, look at all the built-in functions that are included in the FUNCTION.TRU help file. You can search that file for a particular function or you can read Appendix E.

Topic	Page
Definition of a function and its properties	83
Functions that mxodify numbers	84
How to round decimal numbers at a specified digit	85
Trigonometric and logarithmic functions	86
Functions that convert between numbers and strings	88
A function that finds a character in a string	89
How to create substrings	90
Functions that change the case of strings	91
Generating random numbers for simulation	92
Creating a file of random frequencies	94

Figure 7.1*—What you have learned in Chapter 7.*

Program Units

As programs become larger, they are easier to design and write if they are divided into several, separate program units. One unit is always the *main program unit*, the kind of single-unit program that you have written up to this point. There can be only one main program unit and one and only one `END` statement. I always place that statement at the end of the main program unit.

This chapter introduces two other kinds of program units, the *function unit* (also called a programmed function) and the *subroutine unit*. Both of these units are also called *procedures*. A third type of procedure used in graphics, the *picture unit*, is not discussed here. A program can contain as many procedures as you wish. All procedures located after the `END` statement are called *external procedures*.

8.1 MODULAR PROGRAM DESIGN

The process of designing a large program as a collection of units is often called *modular program design*. This type of design has several advantages:

- The program is easier to design.
- The program is easier to write and debug.
- The program is easier to read and understand.
- The program is easier to maintain and modify.
- The program probably contains fewer errors.
- Some of the program units may be used more than once.

After describing function units, I will discuss these advantages in more detail.

The question often arises: At what program size should you start using modular design? My own advice is that when a program grows longer than a full screen or about 25 lines, you should consider more than one unit.

8.2 FUNCTION UNITS

Having looked at some built-in functions in Chapter 7, let's now examine programmed functions or function units. Look at a program containing a programmed function named `CubeRoot`. As you might guess, this function calculates the cube root of its argument. The calling program looks very similar to Example Program 7-1. In Example Program 8-1, a separate function unit is follows the main program unit.

```
! Example Program 8-1
! Using a function unit.

DECLARE FUNCTION CubeRoot
PRINT CubeRoot(27)
END !Main Program

FUNCTION CubeRoot (Nmbr)
    LET CubeRoot = Nmbr^(1/3)
END FUNCTION !CubeRoot
```

The output of this program is the number 3, the cube root of 27.

NOTE: When I refer to a function in this chapter, I normally mean a programmed function unit.

In the main program unit, a new `DECLARE` statement reserves the name `CubeRoot` as a function name and appears as follows:

```
DECLARE FUNCTION CubeRoot
```

If your program has two or more function units, they can all be declared in a single `DECLARE` statement or if you prefer, in multiple `DECLARE` statements. The purpose of declaring a function name is to let the program know that the name is a function name, not a variable name. Without this declaration, a program would have no way to distinguish between the two types of name.

The function unit itself begins with a heading statement

```
FUNCTION CubeRoot (Nmbr)
```

that repeats the name of the function and defines its parameter(s). A parameter is a variable in the procedure that receives information from an argument in the calling unit. In this case, the parameter (`Nmbr`) in the function heading statement corresponds to the function argument (27) in the main program unit. The process of calling the function — using the name `CubeRoot` in the `PRINT` statement — assigns or passes the value 27 to the variable `Nmbr`. You will learn more about passing information to a function in subsequent sections. The function unit ends with a closing statement:

```
END FUNCTION
```

As shown in this example program, an assignment statement within the function unit is always required, it must assign a value — in this case, the cube root of 27 or 3 — to the function name. That is important, a function won't return a value without such an assignment statement.

As mentioned earlier, I always put functions after the main program unit `END` statement, thereby creating external functions. I will explain why later in the chapter.

Why Write a Program in Modular Form?

Let's examine the advantages I listed at the beginning of this chapter.

1. The program is easier to design because you think in terms of functional blocks, not individual program statements. For example, one procedure might identify and open a file of names and phone numbers. Another procedure might dump the entire file into an array. A third procedure might sort the array by name. And so forth.

2. The program is easier to write because each procedure usually solves only one problem. When you are writing the procedure to dump a file into an array, you don't need to be worrying about how to open the file or sort the array.

3. The program is easier to debug because each procedure can be debugged independently. A short procedure is less likely to contain errors and if they exist, it is usually easier to find them.

4. The program is easier to read and understand, to maintain and modify because you are working at any given time only on a single procedure. You have successfully divided one large, sometimes complex job into several smaller tasks that are easier to understand.

The concept of reusing a program unit in the same or a different program is sometimes given as the main reason for modular program design. While the ability to reuse a program unit is important, I don't believe that is the main reason. The advantages of modular program design come primarily from reducing the size of the program unit you are working with at any particular time, thereby reducing the likelihood of making mistakes.

It is true, however, that there are times when a procedure is used more than once in a program. A widely used procedure like a sorting routine might be stored in a library of procedures and called on whenever it is needed in a program. That technique, using library procedures, can save time and effort.

TIP: True BASIC Inc. sells more than ten different pre-written procedure libraries that are a great help when writing large programs. They save you time that would otherwise be spent writing program code.

Many of these advantages of procedures are realized only if the procedures are isolated from each other so that an error in one procedure cannot cause an error in another procedure. I will discuss this matter of isolation later in the chapter.

Challenge Problem 8-1

Before the discussion get more complicated, write a program yourself like Example Program 8-1. Add statements that ask the user for a number and then calculate and display the cube root of that number. Be sure to design your program with a function unit, that is the main point of this exercise.

8.3 SUBROUTINE UNITS

A subroutine performs some task or carries out some action. In contrast to a function, there is no value associated with the subroutine name, the name is used only to identify the unit. Example Program 8-2 uses a subroutine to display a title on the screen, centered between the left and right margins.

```
! Example Program 8-2
! Display a centered screen title.

PRINT "Width of screen in columns? ";
INPUT WidthInCols
INPUT "Title? ", Title$
CALL Center (Title$, WidthInCols)
END !Main Program

SUB Center (Heading$, ScrnWidth)
    CLEAR                                          !Clear the screen
    LET BlankSpace = ScrnWidth - Len(Heading$)               !Get
    LET Indent = BlankSpace / 2                 !indentation value
    FOR Count = 1 TO Indent                   !Display the required
        PRINT " ";                          !number of single spaces
    NEXT Count
    PRINT Heading$                               !Display the heading
END SUB !Center
```

A subroutine is activated by a `CALL` statement in the main program unit, followed by the subroutine name and then in parentheses, its arguments separated by commas.

```
CALL Center (Title$, ColWidth)
```

A DECLARE statement is not needed because the CALL statement serves to identify Center as the name of a subroutine. The arguments in this program happen to be variables, not values. Values, variables, or expressions can all be used as arguments for both functions and subroutines.

Note carefully that the names of arguments and parameters do not have to be the same. They do have to agree, however, in type and position. In this case, the first argument (Title$) and the first parameter (Heading$) must both be strings; the second argument (WidthInCols) and second parameter (ScrnWidth) must both be numbers.

The subroutine unit itself is fairly straightforward. Both the desired title and the width of the screen in columns are passed to the subroutine, from argument to parameter. The screen is cleared, the amount of indentation is calculated, and a sufficient number of spaces are printed so that when the title is displayed, it will appear in the center of the screen. I have added comments in bold face to highlight important statements in the program.

Here is the kind of output produced by Example Program 7-2:

```
Width of screen in columns? 80
Title? ACM5GK2 REPORT
                                 ACM5GK2 REPORT
```

Of course, I had to leave out the effects of the CLEAR statement in order to show you the centered title. Note there are (80 - 14) / 2 or 33 spaces before the title so the value of Indent is 33.

8.4 PROPERTIES OF PROCEDURE UNITS

Let's look next at some of the general properties of procedure units. In particular, I want to discuss how to isolate a procedure from other parts of the program, and the different ways to exchange information between procedures.

Use of Local Variables

Local variables are defined as variables that first appear and are used in a program unit. They are known only in that program unit, they are local to that unit. If external procedures are used — always the case in the example programs in this book — each unit in a True BASIC program has its own local variables. More importantly, the names of these local variables need not be unique.

What do I mean by the phrase "need not be unique?" Variables BlankSpace, Indent, and Count in Example Program 8-2 are all local variables of subroutine Center. Another variable named Indent, for example, could be created as a local variable in the main program unit. The program would now have two variables named `Indent`, one in the main program and one in the subroutine `Center`.

These two variables, each named `Indent`, can exist at the same time and still remain completely independent of one another. The value of `Indent` in the main program unit is stored in one memory location, the value of `Indent` in the subroutine unit is stored in another. There is absolutely no connection between these two local variables located in different program units. Local variables help to isolate one program unit from another. This isolation provided by local variables is one of the most important reasons for using external procedures.

Try the following experiment. Modify Example Program 8-2 by creating a local variable named `Indent` in the main program unit. Insert two new statements, one before and one after the statement that calls subroutine `Center`. A new listing shows the program with the added statements:

```
! Example Program 8-2a
! Display a centered screen title.

PRINT "Width of screen in columns? ";
INPUT WidthInCols
INPUT "Title? ", Title$
LET Indent = 100                                        !new statement
CALL Center (Title$, WidthInCols)
PRINT Indent                                            !new statement
END !Main Program

SUB Center (Heading$, ScrnWidth)
    CLEAR
    LET BlankSpace = ScrnWidth - Len(Heading$)
    LET Indent = BlankSpace / 2
    FOR Count = 1 TO Indent
        PRINT " ";
    NEXT Count
    PRINT Heading$
END SUB !Center
```

Note that local variable `Indent` is first assigned a value of 100 in the main program and then a variable named `Indent` – another local variable `Indent` in subroutine `Center` – is assigned a value of 33 (the value of `BlankSpace/2`). Which value of `Indent` do you think will be displayed by the last `PRINT` statement in the main program?

If you said "100" you are right, I think you understand local variables. Even though `Indent` in the subroutine was assigned a value of 33, the value of `Indent` in the main program is still 100 — they are different variables.

Such independence of local variables, also known as *isolation*, prevents the change of some variable's value in one unit from inadvertently changing the value of a similarly named variable in another unit. It eliminates a common source of program errors. That's why I almost always use external procedures because all their variables are local variables.

Global Variables

The opposite of a local variable is a *global variable*. Older versions of BASIC used only global variables and in large programs, changing an index variable like `Count` on one page might change the value of a variable named `Count` many pages away. It made debugging these programs very difficult.

One or more global variables can be created in a True BASIC program by placing the following statement in the main program unit:

```
PUBLIC Variable1, Variable2,...
```

These global variables are then known in every program unit. As an experiment, try adding the statement

```
PUBLIC Indent
```

to Example Program 8-2a and see what a difference it makes.

Any procedures, either functions or subroutines, preceding the program's `END` statement become *internal procedures* and have semi-global variables. These variables are known throughout the main program unit – that is, in any statement preceding the `END` statement – but not in any external procedures.

If local variables isolate one program unit from another, how can units communicate with each other? One answer is through global variables but that can cause other problems. A better answer is through their arguments and parameters, the next topic of discussion.

Use of Arguments and Parameters

Arguments are the expressions following the procedure name in a statement that calls a procedure unit — function or subroutine. As noted previously, arguments can be values, variables, or expressions. Looking back at Example Program 8-2, `Title$` and `WidthInCols` are arguments. In Example Program 8-1, the calling statement is `PRINT CubeRoot(27)` and the argument is 27.

Parameters are the variables in parentheses in a procedure heading statement. Parameters can only be variables — values and expressions are not allowed. Looking again at Example Program 8-2, `Heading$` and `ScrnWidth` are parameters. In Example Program 8-1, `Nmbr` is the parameter.

You must learn the meaning of these two words, *argument* and *parameter*, and not confuse them. Unfortunately, some programmers and even programming books are sloppy and use the two words interchangeably.

Information is always passed forward from an argument to its corresponding parameter. In some cases — and *only* with subroutines — information can be passed back to the argument from its corresponding parameter. This is the way that subroutines communicate with other subroutines and the main program unit.

Behavior of Functions

First, I want to discuss the behavior of functions. Communication flows in *only one direction* from function arguments in the calling program to function parameters in the function unit. The *values* of function arguments are passed to the corresponding function parameters. The only way that a function can send information back to the calling program is through a value assigned to the function name.

If the preceding statement is not perfectly clear, please read it again. Functions are strongly isolated. There is *no* way that a function parameter (in the function heading statement) can pass information back to a function argument (in the function calling statement). This sentence implies that only a single value — the value assigned to the function name — can be passed back to the calling program.

Behavior of Subroutines

Now let's consider how subroutines behave. Variables used as arguments can both send and receive information because in subroutines, the *address* of an argument variable is passed to the corresponding parameter variable. The argument variable and the parameter variable now share the same address or memory location and any change made in the value of one is immediately known to the other. The result is two-way communication between the calling unit and the called unit.

Looking back once more at Example Program 8-2, all the arguments are variables. `Title$` and `Heading$` share the same address so they share the same value. They can communicate with each other in either direction. Similarly, `WidthInCols` and `ScrnWidth` share the same address and value.

Values and expressions used as arguments pass information in only one direction, from the calling unit to the called subroutine. The value of the argument is assigned to a temporary variable and the address of that temporary variable is passed to the corresponding parameter variable. The temporary variable is then deleted after its value has been stored in the parameter variable and so it no longer exists. No information can be passed back to the calling unit. In this case – a value or expression argument – the parameter variable in a subroutine behaves just like a local variable.

An Example of How to Pass Information

Here is a simple little program that demonstrates the behavior of subroutine arguments and parameters:

```
! Example Program 8-3
! Communication with a subroutine.

LET Number = 5
PRINT "Before calling subroutine, ";
PRINT "Number is"; Number
CALL New (Number)
PRINT "After calling subroutine, ";
PRINT "Number is"; Number
END !Main Program

SUB New (Nmbr)
    LET Nmbr = 10
END SUB !New
```

The following output is produced:

```
Before calling subroutine, Number is 5
After calling subroutine, Number is 10
```

When the subroutine is called, the address of variable `Number` is passed to it. The value of `Nmbr` is changed in the subroutine and because this is the same variable as — has the same address as — the variable `Number` in the calling unit, the value of `Number` also changed in the main program. There is two-way communication between the calling unit and the subroutine.

To see how the program behaves when the argument is an expression, put an extra set of parentheses around `Number` in the `CALL` statement. In True BASIC, that small change is sufficient to create an expression:

```
CALL New ((Number))  !note the extra parentheses
```

An expression behaves differently from a variable — this output is produced:

```
Before calling subroutine, Number is 5
After calling subroutine, Number is 5
```

Why is there a difference? Remember that when the argument is an expression, its value — the value of `(Number)` — is assigned to a temporary variable. The address of the temporary variable is passed to the subroutine unit and its value is assigned to the corresponding parameter variable, `Nmbr`. The temporary variable is then deleted and because an address for the temporary variable no longer exists, any change in the value of `Nmbr` cannot be passed back to the calling program. One-way communication is established and the value of variable `Number` remains 5.

TIP: Remember that *arguments* are always in the calling statement, *parameters* are always in the procedure heading statement. It is easy to confuse the two words.

As mentioned previously, a value argument behaves just like an expression argument. I have not included an example program but you can easily write one yourself and observe that this statement is true. Remember my advice to learn by writing short experimental programs yourself.

Communication between subroutines through arguments and parameters is not easy to understand, and frankly, it's not easy to explain. In the end, it all boils down to these two facts. If you want isolation, use *values* or *expressions* as arguments If you want two-way communication, use *variables* as arguments. Parameters, on the other hand, must always be variables.

Challenge Problem 8-2

Write a short program with a subroutine. I suggest a file reading program like Example Program 5-3. Pass as a parameter the file path name that is specified by the user.. The channel or file number is known only in the subroutine; I explain in the next chapter how to pass channel numbers as parameters.

Write another short program that uses an external function to make a calculation. The function should contain some engineering formula. Remember that a function returns only a single value.

8.5 BRIDGE INSPECTION, Part III

You may remember the bridge inspection programs in Chapter 5. One displayed an individual bridge's natural frequency, as measured by five different inspection teams. Another analyzed the consistency of frequency measurements among the five teams. Now that you know about procedures, it seems appropriate to combine these programs together into a new, larger, menu-driven program. The new program takes advantage of modular design.

Menu-Driven Programs

I use the term *menu-driven program* to describe the type of program that displays a menu of action items on the screen and lets the user make a choice. Example Program 8-4 provides only three items in its menu but the program is designed so it is easy to add additional items. In all but one case, the choice of an item results in the calling of a subroutine that takes the desired action. In the example program, one subroutine displays an individual bridge's natural frequency, while another analyzes variations in the measured frequency. If you want to add another item to the menu, you just need to modify the menu slightly and write one or more additional subroutines.

For the first time in an example program, I introduce limited error checking of user input. A program designed for general use is really not acceptable if bad input from the user produces error messages that mean nothing to that user. As you may have noticed already, True BASIC error messages are usually designed to help the programmer, not an end user of the program. This chapter introduces limited error checking – a general method of error checking and trapping is discussed in Chapter 9.

Here then is Example Program 8-4. It is considerably larger than any preceding program, especially because I have added many extra remarks in bold face to help you follow the program logic.

```
! Example Program 8-4
! This program provides a menu for selecting
! information on the natural frequencies of bridges.

! Define an array to hold all the frequencies.
DIM BridgeRecord(1:23, 1:5)

CLEAR                                              !Clear the screen
CALL LoadArray (BridgeRecord(,))                    !Load data into
                                                         !the array
DO
  PRINT                                    !Display the menu choices
  PRINT "0. Exit the program"
  PRINT "1. Select a bridge, display its frequency"
  PRINT "2. Display each team's average measurement"
  PRINT
  INPUT prompt "Enter choice: ": Choice       !0, 1 or 2
  SELECT CASE Choice
     CASE 0                                            !Choice is 0
       EXIT DO                                 !Exit the loop and stop
     CASE 1                                            !Choice is 1
       CALL BridgeAverage (BridgeRecord(,))            !Display the
                               !measurements of specified bridge
     CASE 2                                            !Choice is 2
       CALL TeamAverage (BridgeRecord(,))              !Display the
                               !average measurement by each team
     CASE ELSE                            !Invalid choice was entered
       PRINT "Error: Enter 0, 1, or 2."                ! Error msg.
  END SELECT
LOOP while Choice <> 0                       !Loop back if Choice <> 0
END  !Main Program
```

```
SUB BridgeAverage (BridgeRecord(,))
! Ask user to enter a bridge number and
! display frequencies measured for that bridge.
! See Example Program 6-11.

  PRINT
  CALL BridgeNumber (Bridge)                       !Read first number
  DO UNTIL Bridge = 0                              !Exit loop if zero
    PRINT "TEAM:        ";                    !Display the line title
    FOR Team = 1 TO 5                                !Display all the
      PRINT USING " #   ": Team;                !number designation
    NEXT Team                                           !of each team
    PRINT "Average"                                 !Start a new line
    PRINT "FREQUENCY:   ";                    !Display the line title
    LET Sum = 0                         !Reset Sum to zero
    FOR Team = 1 TO 5                     !For all teams, get each
      LET Temp = BridgeRecord(Bridge, Team)               !frequency
      PRINT USING "#.#  ": Temp;                     !and display it
      LET Sum = Sum + Temp                     !Add frequency to Sum
    NEXT Team                                       !from other teams
    LET Average = Sum/5                        !Display the average
    PRINT USING "###.#": Average;                !natural frequency
    PRINT                                           !Start a new line
    PRINT                                            !and skip a line
    CALL BridgeNumber (Bridge)                 !Read the next bridge
    LOOP                                      ! number and loop back
END SUB !BridgeAverage

SUB TeamAverage (BridgeRecord(,))
! Calculate the average frequency
! measured by each of the teams.
! See Example Program 6-12.

  PRINT                                        !Display a blank line
  PRINT "Average of each team's frequency"                  !and two
  PRINT "measurements for all bridges:"              !heading lines
  PRINT
  PRINT "TEAM:   ";                                  !Display a label
  FOR Team = 1 TO 5                                      !and all the
    PRINT USING " #    ": Team;                              !bridge
  NEXT Team                                                 !numbers
  PRINT                                              !Start a new row
  PRINT "FREQ:  ";                                   !Display a label
  FOR Team = 1 TO 5                                   !For each team,
    LET Sum = 0                        !initialize Sum to zero and
    FOR Bridge = 1 TO 23                     !add up the frequency
      LET Freq = BridgeRecord(Bridge, Team)            !measurements
      LET Sum = Sum + Freq                                   !of all
    NEXT Bridge                                         !the bridges
```

```
      LET Average = Sum/23                                   !Calculate and
      PRINT USING "#.##  ": Average;                           !display the
    NEXT Team                                            !average frequency
    PRINT                                                   !of all bridges
  END SUB !TeamAverage

  SUB LoadArray (BridgeRecord(,))
  ! Read file data and assign to an array.
  ! See Example Program 6-10

    ! Change value of Path$ as required.
    LET Path$ = "A:\FREQS.DAT"
    OPEN #1: name Path$, access input
    DO until End #1                          !Stop loop at end of file
      INPUT #1: Bridge, Team, Frequency           !Read line of data
      LET BridgeRecord(Bridge, Team) = Frequency                   !and
                                  !assign frequency to an array element
    LOOP                                !Read the next line in the file
    CLOSE #1                                 !Close file after reading
  END SUB !LoadArray

  SUB BridgeNumber (Bridge)
  ! Returns a valid bridge number.

    DO
      PRINT "Bridge number(0 to stop)? ";                   !Prompt and
      INPUT prompt "": Bridge                          !read bridge number
                                                             !If number is
      IF Bridge > 23 OR Bridge < 0 then                          !invalid,
        PRINT "Enter a non-negative number";                     !display
        PRINT " less than or equal to 23."                      !an error
        PRINT                                                    !message
      END IF
    LOOP while Bridge > 23 OR Bridge < 0
                          !Loop back if number is invalid
  END SUB !BridgeNumber
```

An example of program output follows:

```
0. Exit the program
1. Select a bridge, display its frequency
2. Display each team's average measurement

Enter your choice: 1

Bridge number (0 to stop)? 3
TEAM:              1    2    3    4    5   Average
FREQUENCY:       3.9  4.0  4.4  4.2  3.8     4.1

Bridge number (0 to stop)? 7
```

```
TEAM:           1    2    3    4    5   Average
FREQUENCY:    3.9  3.9  3.7  3.7  3.8     3.8

Bridge number (0 to stop)? 0

0. Exit the program
1. Select a bridge, display its frequency
2. Display each team's average measurement

Enter your choice: 2

Average of each team's frequency
measurements for all bridges:

TEAM:    1     2     3     4     5
FREQ:  5.43  5.44  5.58  5.43  5.44

0. Exit the program
1. Select skater, display scores
2. Display judge's average score

Enter your choice: 0
```

In earlier versions of True BASIC you may have to press a key – any key – once or twice to display the editing screen again.

Procedures Calling Procedures

A new concept introduced in the preceding program is that of one procedure unit calling another procedure unit. Subroutine `BridgeAverage` needs a user-supplied bridge number. This subroutine calls another subroutine named `BridgeNumber` that prompts the user for a number and checks the entered number to make certain it is valid. The main reason for making `BridgeNumber` a separate procedure is that it is used twice in this program and will likely be used again if other choices are added to the menu.

Array Arguments and Parameters

The array `BridgeRecord` is defined in the main program unit with a `DIM` statement and thus cannot be defined again in another unit. If you try to do so, you get an error message saying "duplicate definition." `BridgeRecord` is a local variable in the main program unit.

You can pass an array to another unit as an argument. You must use an array variable as the argument, not an array expression or value — there is no single number that represents the value of an entire array. True BASIC contains no array functions or expressions. To distinguish an array from a simple variable, a set of parentheses containing zero or more commas is used to identify an array *parameter* variable. If the array has one dimension, leave its parentheses empty, if it has two dimensions, put one comma inside the parentheses, and so forth.

An optional set of parentheses can also be used to identify an array *argument* variable – I usually include them just to remind myself that the argument is an array – but they are not required. In Example Program 8-4, you find both an array argument and an array parameter named `BridgeRecord(,)`. Note the single comma in the parentheses – `BridgeRecord` has two dimensions.

Global versus Local Variables

If you want any of the subroutines to read or modify the contents of the array, you must pass `BridgeRecord` to them as an argument. In fact, the array is required in all but one subroutine. Since both argument and parameter are variables, two-way communication is established and the current value of `BridgeRecord` is known in each subroutine where it appears as a parameter — it is effectively a local variable in each of these subroutines.

At this point, you might wonder why `BridgeRecord` is not defined as a global variable. That's a good question and using a global variable is a reasonable alternative. One reason why I designed the program to pass `BridgeRecord` as a parameter is that program units and their parameters are the subject of this chapter.

There is also another, more important reason. I expect this program to be modified and lengthened in the future. If that is done, there may be some disadvantage in making `BridgeRecord` available to a procedure, as yet unwritten. If I define `BridgeRecord` as a global variable, I have no choice, it will always be available to any procedure, present or future. Part of good design is leaving as many options open as possible.

Error Checking

In the subroutine `BridgeNumber`, I introduce the concept of error checking. This subroutine will not accepts a bridge number that is less than zero or greater than 23. If an invalid bridge number is entered, the user is told that the entry is invalid and asked to try again.

The statement I just made is not quite accurate — the user is told what bridge numbers are valid, not that the entered number is invalid. It is much better to tell users what they should do, rather than tell them only that what they did was wrong. This is sometime described as an aspect of *user-friendly* programming, unfortunately a much over-used term but an important consideration when writing programs.

Notice that error checking is also done at the menu level. If you type in any character other than 0, 1 or 2, the following message is displayed:

```
Error: Enter number 0, 1 or 2.
```

You are then given an opportunity to make another menu choice. Remember that this error message will have to be changed if the menu is enlarged.

Compound Logical Expressions

Notice also that the logical expressions in the subroutine `BridgeNumber` are more complicated than those used previously. If you need assistance, consult your manual or review the material in Chapter 5.

Challenge Problem 8-3

Write a program that adds another menu choice to Example Program 8-4. You may make your own choice but if you can't think of anything, here is a suggestion.

Create a list of all bridges and their average natural frequencies. Display this list in two columns, one for bridge numbers, the other for frequencies. Write all information on a file named RESULTS.DAT.

What You Have Learned

Modular design of programs with external or independent procedures is a technique that all programmers should learn. This technique will become even more important in the future as graphics-oriented languages (like the latest versions of True BASIC and Microsoft Visual Basic) become widely used.

I think the hardest part of modular design is understanding how arguments and parameters work. Remember these points:

- Arguments are part of the calling statement, parameters are part of the procedure heading.
- Parameters are always variables.
- Function arguments always provide one-way communication – a value can be passed back only through the function name.
- Subroutine arguments that are variables provide two-way communication – the address of the argument variable is passed to the subroutine parameter.
- Subroutine arguments that are expressions or values provide only one-way communication – only the value of the expression argument or value argument is passed to the subroutine parameter.

Topic	Page
The meaning of modular program design	97
Use and syntax of programmed function units	98
Advantages of modular program design	99
Use and syntax of subroutine units	100
Local variables: advantages and disadvantages	101
Global variables: advantages and disadvantages	103
How arguments and parameters work	104
Passing information between program units	105
Designing a modular program with multiple units	106
How procedures call other procedures	110
Passing arrays as arguments	110
Global versus local variables	111
Error checking in programs	111

Figure 8.1*—What you have learned in Chapter 8.*

More Programs

In the first eight chapters, you have learned all the fundamental skills needed to create True BASIC programs. What you need now is lots of practice. As in writing, first you learn grammar and spelling, then you learn to write by writing, writing, and more writing. Where do you turn for examples of good writing? You read as many of the works of successful authors as you can.

The same concepts apply to designing and writing computer programs. This chapter exposes you to some additional fundamental ideas in programming. Read these example programs, modify them as you see fit, run them over and over again, and you will gradually learn to write satisfying programs of your own. Good luck!

9.1 PROGRAMS THAT MEASURE TIME

It is not only interesting but often important to know how long it takes to accomplish some task in a program. Your computer has an internal clock that can be accessed from True BASIC by the `Time` function. This function returns a value that is the number of seconds since the last midnight. You can use the `Time` function to record the time of starting and stopping a specific action and then the difference between these two values is the time required to complete the action. Here is an example program:

```
! Example Program 9-1
! Calculate the time required to write a
! text file. User specifies line content
! and number of lines. Each line contains
! the same string of characters.

CLEAR
PRINT "Enter full path name of file: ";
LINE INPUT prompt "": PathName$
PRINT "Enter contents of each line: ";
LINE INPUT prompt "": Line$
PRINT "Enter the number of lines: ";
INPUT prompt "": Limit
OPEN #1: name PathName$, create newold
ERASE #1 !in case it already exists
```

```
LET StartTime = Time
FOR Count = 1 to Limit
    PRINT #1: Line$
NEXT Count
CLOSE #1
LET StopTime = Time
LET TotalTime = StopTime - StartTime
LET DisplayTime = Round(TotalTime, 2)
PRINT
PRINT "Time to write the file is"; DisplayTime;
PRINT "seconds"
END
```

On my computer, when I specified that I was writing to a fixed disk, that the contents of each line would be a string of 10 characters, and that the file would contain 10,000 lines, I got the following output:

```
Time to write the file is 4.89 seconds
```

You will probably get different results because your computer is faster or slower than mine.

NOTE: A computer clock operates at a very high frequency, allowing time differences of a millionth of a second to be detected. The `Time` function, however, is not that sensitive. It measures time only to the nearest hundredth of a second.

Another question that can be answered by experiment is how changes in program design can affect speed of execution. Let's look at the difference in speed when different methods are used to make numeric calculations. Here is a specific example, a program that calculates the total volume of a number of spheres with constant radius. The program reads as follows:

```
! Example Program 9-2
! Calculate the volume of N spheres
! where number N is entered by the user.

CLEAR
LET Radius = 22.3 !units
LET Fraction = 4/3 !units
INPUT prompt "Number of spheres? ": N
PRINT

PRINT "Case 1: Multiply the volume of one sphere"
PRINT "by the number of spheres."
LET Sum = 0
LET StartTime = Time
LET Sum = N * (4 * Pi * Radius ^ 3)/3
LET StopTime = Time
CALL DisplayResults (Sum, StartTime, StopTime)
```

```
PRINT "Case 2: Use variables, multiplication,"
PRINT "and a loop to calculate total volume."
LET Sum = 0
LET StartTime = Time
FOR Count = 1 to N
  LET Volume = Fraction*Pi*Radius*Radius*Radius
  LET Sum = Sum + Volume
NEXT Count
LET StopTime = Time
CALL DisplayResults (Sum, StartTime, StopTime)

PRINT "Case 3: Use variables, exponentiation,"
PRINT "and a loop to calculate total volume."
LET Sum = 0
LET StartTime = Time
FOR Count = 1 to N
  LET Volume = Fraction*Pi*Radius^3
  LET Sum = Sum + Volume
NEXT Count
LET StopTime = Time
CALL DisplayResults (Sum, StartTime, StopTime)

PRINT "Case 4: Use numbers, exponentiation,"
PRINT "and a loop to calculate total volume."
LET Sum = 0
LET StartTime = Time
FOR Count = 1 to N
  LET Volume = (4 * 3.14159 * (22.3^3))/3
  LET Sum = Sum + Volume
NEXT Count
LET StopTime = Time
CALL DisplayResults (Sum, StartTime, StopTime)
END !Main Program

SUB DisplayResults (Sum, StartTime, StopTime)
! Display the results of calculations.

  LET CalcTime = StopTime - StartTime
  LET Volume = Sum/1000000
  PRINT using "Volume is ###.#": Volume;
  PRINT " million cubic units"
  PRINT "Calculation time is ";
  PRINT using "##.## seconds": CalcTime
  PRINT
END SUB !DisplayResults
```

Here are some typical results:

```
Number of spheres? 10000

Case 1: Multiply the volume of one sphere
by the number of spheres.
Volume is 464.5 million cubic units
Calculation time is  .00 seconds

Case 2: Use variables, multiplication,
and a loop to calculate total volume.
Volume is 464.5 million cubic units
Calculation time is 1.48 seconds

Case 3: Use variables, exponentiation,
and a loop to calculate total volume.
Volume is 464.5 million cubic units
Calculation time is 2.80 seconds

Case 4: Use numbers, exponentiation,
and a loop to calculate total volume.
Volume is 464.5 million cubic units
Calculation time is 3.08 seconds
```

It should be no surprise that multiplication is much faster than a loop, as shown by the short time — too short to register — for the Case 1 calculation. Never use a loop structure if multiplication will do the job.

It may surprise you, however, that the Case 3 calculation takes more time, almost twice as much time, as the Case 2 calculation. Multiplication on a computer — at least on my computer — is a much faster process than exponentiation (raising to a power). Finally, most languages, including True BASIC, execute an expression more quickly if it contains variables rather than numbers, so Case 3 is slightly faster than Case 4. Remember all these points if you are writing a program where speed of execution is critical.

In summary, this section shows you how to measure the speed of a program. Sometimes programs, or at least sections of programs, need to be executed as quickly as possible. You now know how to measure execution time and determine which programming structure produces the shortest time.

Spend a little time examining this program and its results. It is important that you thoroughly understand how program design can affect speed of execution.

Challenge Problem 9-1

You are asked to calculate the volume of a rectangular box whose dimensions are entered by the user. You have a choice of making the calculation in the main program or in a procedure. Is there any difference in the accuracy of the two methods? Is there any difference in the time of calculation? Is the time difference significant?

Your computer clock may not be sensitive enough to measure the time difference for a single box. To answer the questions, you may have to calculate the volume of a large number of boxes of the specified size.

9.2 ERROR TRAPPING and HANDLING

There are different types of program errors. The True BASIC editor does a good job catching syntax errors when you first try to run a program and letting you know about them. I expect you have already experienced that process. These syntax errors can usually be corrected easily with the editor. In fact, they *must* be corrected before you can execute the program.

A more bothersome type of error is the error of logic, usually resulting from a mistake in logic when the program was designed or written. Your program may run perfectly but produce meaningless results. These errors are sometimes called "hair-pulling errors", the kind of errors that can make a beginning programmer very frustrated. The way to find errors in logic is to follow the debugging procedures discussed in Chapter 4.

Some of these errors in logic are also classified as run-time errors, they usually make the program stop and in all cases display an error message. The error message may make sense to you, the programmer, but it probably makes no sense at all to someone using your program. Other run-time errors are user errors – the result of a mistake made by the user like entering an invalid file name.

In any case, before you can consider a program finished, you must correct all errors in logic and do whatever you can to reduce user errors. True BASIC provides a facility for *trapping* run-time errors, allowing the user to correct those errors that are correctable and continue executing the program.

Errors produced in a specified block of statements, the protected block, can be trapped and then handled by another block of statements, the error handler block. This latter block of statements is not executed unless a run-time error occurs. Here is the syntax:

```
WHEN ERROR IN
     protected block
USE
     error handler block
END WHEN
```

An error is often called an exception but I will continue to use the shorter word .

TIP: Get in the habit of adding error trapping and handling to programs you develop. These techniques make it much easier for users with limited experience to run your programs.

The Protected Block

The *protected block* can be any sequence of statements in the main program unit or in a procedure unit, but it cannot include a procedure heading statement. It can include a call to a procedure in which case the procedure code is also protected. In most applications, the protected block is a short sequence of a half dozen or so statements. It may only be a single statement.

The Error Handler Block

The *error handler block* is another sequence of statements that is executed only if there is a run-time error in the protected block. Under normal circumstances, the program skips over the error handler block and continues with the first statement after the `END WHEN` statement.

The EXTYPE and EXTEXT$ Functions

Two system functions are particularly useful in the error handler block. The numeric function `EXTYPE` returns an error number when a run-time error occurs. These numbers are listed in Appendix G. The value of `EXTYPE` can be used to make a decision about what action to take in the error handler block.

The string function `EXTEXT$` returns the specific error message — also listed in Appendix G. When error trapping is in operation, this message is not printed automatically because the error handler block is invoked instead. The value of `EXTEXT$` can be displayed, if desired, or used in any other manner.

Here is an example program using error trapping during the calculation of a square root:

```
! Example Program 9-3
! Trap any errors while calculating
! the square root of a number converted
! from a string entry.

LET NoError$ = "false"
DO
  LINE INPUT prompt "Enter number: ": Value$
  WHEN error in !protected block
    LET Number = Val(Value$)
    LET Result = Sqr(Number)
    PRINT "Square root of "; Value$; " is";
    PRINT Round(Result, 2)
    LET NoError$ = "true"

  USE !error handler block
    IF Extype = 3005 then !Sqr of a negative number
      PRINT "Enter a positive number"
```

```
    ELSEIF Extype = 4001 then !Improper Val string
      PRINT "Enter proper numeric format"
    ELSE
      PRINT "Unexpected error: "; Extext$
    END IF
  END WHEN

LOOP until NoError$ = "true"
END
```

The `LINE INPUT` statement accepts any string of characters, but if the `Val` function cannot convert that string into a number — the string has the wrong format — then the error handler block is invoked. Similarly, if the number is negative so its square root is not a real number, the error handler block is invoked again. Finally, if there is any other error in the protected block, an "Unexpected error" message is displayed with the appropriate error message text. Look up error types 3005 and 4001 in Appendix G.

Using a Binary Flag

A variable is often used as a binary marker – usually called a flag. What do I mean by a flag? I mean a variable that can have one of two values and indicates when some change in the program has taken place. The two values are often the strings "true" and "false."

In this program, the flag variable is named `NoError$`. It is set to "false" at the beginning of the program and if all statements in the protected block are executed without error, it is reset to "true."

Here is an example of program output:

```
Enter number: -33a
Enter proper numeric format
Enter number: -33
Enter a positive number
Enter number: 33
Square root of 33 is 5.74
```

Error trapping is an example of good defensive programming. You should anticipate the possibility of run-time errors and develop plans to handle them when they occur. Nothing is more discouraging to the user of a program than to have the program suddenly stop and display a message that seems to make no sense.

9.3 PROGRAMS TO SORT LISTS

Sorting is an important task in many computer applications. There are probably more commercial computers running sort procedures than any other utility program. If you have a list of names, you may want to sort them alphabetically as the first step in an examination of the list. If you have a list of numbers such as test results, you may want to sort them numerically, starting with the highest or lowest value. In this situation, there may be a name associated with each number and as the numbers are sorted, each name must remain attached to the correct number. More about that later.

Much research has been devoted to sorting methods or algorithms. If the list to be sorted is long, then speed of sorting is important. If the list is short, however, other characteristics of a sorting algorithm like ease-of-use and simplicity may be more important than speed.

TIP: What do I mean by long and short lists? As a rough rule of thumb for personal computers, we might agree that 1000 names or less is a short list, while more than 1000 names is a long list. I admit the choice is arbitrary but it seems to work pretty well.

Bubble Sort Algorithm

The next example program introduces a simple sorting algorithm called the *bubble sort algorithm*. Let's use it to sort a list of numbers in an array into ascending numerical order, meaning that the smallest number is at the beginning of the list and the largest is at the end. Here, in words, is what the program must do.

Scanning the List

The computer program goes through the list of numbers to be sorted, from one end of the list to the other, comparing numbers in pairs. The first pair consists of the first and second numbers in the list, the next pair consists of the second and third numbers, and so forth. This process is called *scanning the list*.

Checking Pairs of Values

If a pair is in the wrong numerical order (not ascending order), the computer program interchanges the two numbers. If a pair is in the correct numerical order (ascending order), the computer program moves on to the next pair.

Interchanging Values

In most computer languages, including True BASIC, a third temporary variable must be used when interchanging two numbers. To interchange the numeric values stored in variables `A` and `B`, assign the value of `A` to a temporary variable, next assign the value of B to A, and finally assign the value of the temporary variable to B. The program statements might look like this:

```
LET Temp = A   !assign value of A to Temp
LET A = B      !assign value of B to A
LET B = Temp   !assign value of Temp to B
```

No More Interchanges

Each time you start to scan the list, set the value of the flag variable Sorted$ to "true." If you make an interchange of list values during this scan of the list, change the flag value to "false." You examine the flag value at the end of each scan, and if it is "true," you know that no interchanges were made during the last scan through the list and thus the list must be in sorted order.

First Scan	1	7	3	2	5
	1	**3**	**7**	2	5
	1	3	**2**	**7**	5
	1	3	2	**5**	**7**
Second Scan	1	3	2	5	7
	1	**2**	**3**	5	7
Third Scan	1	2	3	5	7

Figure 9.1*—Sorting a list with bubble-sort.*

A diagram often helps to explain a sorting process. Fig. 9.1 shows the bubble-sort algorithm sorting a list of five numbers. The bold-faced and underlined numbers denote a pair that has just been interchanged. Note how large numbers move or "bubble up" to the top – in this case, the right end – of the list. No interchange is made during the third scan, indicating that the list is sorted

The Bubble Sort Subroutine

A subroutine is used for the actual sorting. A one-dimensional array named SortList contains N numeric values. Each element in the array is a number. Both SortList and N are passed to the subroutine.

```
SUB BubbleSort (SortList(), N)
! Use the bubble-sort algorithm to sort
! an array containing N numeric elements.
  DO
    LET Sorted$ = "true"
    FOR Index := 1 to (N - 1)
```

```
      IF SortList(Index) > SortList(Index + 1) then
        LET Temp = SortList(Index)
        LET SortList(Index) = SortList(Index + 1)
        LET SortList(Index + 1) = Temp
        LET Sorted$ = "false"
      END IF
    NEXT Index
  LOOP until Sorted$ = "true"
END SUB !BubbleSort
```

Pairs of list values, denoted by `SortList(Index+1)` and `SortList(Index)`, are compared and interchanged if not in sorted order. Note that `Index`, the `FOR` loop control variable, has a final value of `N - 1`. If `Index` were assigned a value of `N`, the program would try to compare array elements `SortList(N)` and `SortList(N+1)` and would produce unpredictable results because no number has been assigned to the latter element.

Referring to the program, the `FOR` loop performs a single scan of the list. The `IF` statement performs a swap if two elements in the list must be interchanged. The `DO` loop continues until no more swaps can be made.

Ascending versus Descending Order

This subroutine sorts a list of items in ascending order. To sort in descending order, reverse the logical sense of the comparison statement, changing it to the following statement:

```
SortList(Index) < SortList(Index + 1)
```

Sorting a File

A common problem is the need to sort a file of numbers or names. I assume that your computer has enough memory to allow the entire file to be placed in an array variable. If this assumption is true, sorting the file contents is fairly easy and quick. The following tasks must be carried out:

- Read the values from a file and assign them to an array.
- Sort the array in memory.
- Write the sorted array back on a file, usually a different file.

If the contents of the file are too large to hold in memory, then the problem (especially with a text file) is much more difficult and beyond the scope of this book.

Before assigning values from a file to an array, you must determine and then define the size of the array in your program. When you write the program, however, you don't know many values are stored in the file. What can you do?

There are two possible solutions. One solution is to make the array large enough to hold all the values in the largest file you will ever use. That's kind of a tough problem, isn't it? How can you determine what is the largest file that might ever be read by the program you are writing now? About all you can do is make a reasonable guess of maximum file size, like 500 values, for example. If you have a file with less than 500 values, you will only partially fill the array — that does no harm. Remember that you are limited on maximum array size by the amount of memory in your computer. You will need to do some experimenting to determine the maximum array size that your computer can handle.

TIP: If you are working with a partially filled array, it is a good idea to assign a sentinel value to the element immediately following the last data element. A sentinel tells you when you have reached the end of valid data in the array.

Another and probably better solution is to redimension your array after you find out how many values are in the file. The only disadvantage is that it takes a little more time. First, read through the file and count the number of values. Second, use a new statement, the `MAT REDIM` statement, to redimension your array. The syntax is

```
MAT REDIM Array(LowerLimit to UpperLimit)
```

where `Array` is the name of the array and `LowerLimit` and `UpperLimit` are numeric values, variables, or expressions that determine the number of values that can be stored in the array. Remember that you cannot use variables or expressions for index limits in a `DIM` statement, only in a `MAT REDIM` statement. By the way, the word `MAT` stands for matrix, a mathematician's name for an array.

Passing Channel Numbers

You used a file with a subroutine in the preceding chapter, Example Program 8-4, in a situation where the file was opened, used, and closed again within the same program unit. There are times, however, when you wish to open a file in the main program unit or another procedure, and then use that file in a different procedure. How do you pass information about an open file to another procedure, using the mechanism of arguments and parameters?

The method in True BASIC is very simple but there is a limitation – it works only with subroutines, *not* with functions. If you need to use a file in a function, you must open it in that function and then close it in the function when you are finished.

The way to pass information about an opened file to a subroutine is to treat the channel (file) number as just another argument or parameter. For example, let's assume you open a file as #1 in the main program unit. You want to use this file in a subroutine named `FillArray`. You also want to pass a one-dimensional array argument named

`List` and a numeric variable named `Count` to that subroutine. Here is what your calling statement might look like:

```
CALL FillArray (List(), Count, #1)
```

The corresponding heading statement in the subroutine might be the following:

```
SUB FillArray (List(), N, #9)
```

You already know that names `Count` and `N` refer to the same numeric variable. In the same way, channel numbers #1 and #9 refer to the same file. That file is know as file #1 in the main program but as file #9 in the subroutine. The channel number must be a numeric value between 1 and 99, it cannot be a numeric variable or expression. The symbol "#" must precede the channel number.

This syntax structure allows you to write general purpose subroutines that can be used in other programs without having to change the names of variables or channel numbers. Look at the subroutines `OpenFile`, `FillArray`, and `WriteArray` in Example Program 9-4 to see how it works.

Testing the Bubble-Sort Subroutine

The next example program is designed to sort a list of numbers. It assumes that the numbers are stored in a text file, one number per line. The length of the list is limited by the amount of available memory, but there should be no difficulty sorting a list of several hundred numbers. Here is an outline of the program:

- Ask the user for a file name and open an input file.
- Ask the user for a file name and open an output file.
- Calculate the length of the list, declare an array of adequate size.
- Read data from the input file into the array.
- Sort the array.
- Write the sorted array to the output file.

Here is the program itself:

```
 Example Program 9-4
! Read a list of numbers from a text
! file, use the bubble sort algorithm
! to sort this list, and write the sorted
! list to another text file.

DIM List(1:1) !index limits to be changed
CALL OpenFile ("Input file name", "old", #1)
CALL OpenFile ("Output file name", "newold", #2)
CALL FillArray (List(), Count, #1)
```

```
PRINT
CALL DisplayArray (List(), Count, "Unsorted:")
CALL BubbleSort (List(), Count)
PRINT
CALL DisplayArray (List(), Count, "Sorted:")
CALL WriteArray (List(), Count, #2)
PRINT
PRINT "The sorted list is in the output file."
END !Main Program

SUB OpenFile (Prompt$, Mode$, #9)
! Open a file as "outin" for reading or writing.
   PRINT Prompt$;
   LINE INPUT FileName$
   OPEN #9: name FileName$, create Mode$
   IF Mode$ = "newold" then
      ERASE #9 !erase existing file to write
   END IF
END SUB !OpenFile

SUB BubbleSort (List(), N)
! Use the bubble sort algorithm to sort an
! array containing N numeric elements.
   DO
     LET Sorted$ = "true"
     FOR I = 1 to (N - 1)
       IF List(I) > List(I+1) then
         LET Temp = List(I)
         LET List(I) = List(I+1)
         LET List(I+1) = Temp
         LET Sorted$ = "false"
       END IF
     NEXT I
   LOOP until Sorted$ = "true"
END SUB !BubbleSort

SUB DisplayArray (List(), NumOfItems, Title$)
! Display a short, single-line list
! of N numbers on the screen.
   PRINT Title$
   FOR Index = 1 to NumOfItems
      PRINT using "#####"; List(Index);
   NEXT Index
   PRINT
END SUB !DisplayArray

SUB FillArray (List(), N, #7)
! Read a list of numbers from a text
! file and assign them to an array,
! First count the items,
```

```
      LET N = 0
      DO until End #7
         INPUT #7: Dummy
         LET N = N + 1
      LOOP

   ! then redimension and fill the array.
      MAT REDIM List(1:N)
      RESET #7: begin !move to beginning of file
      FOR Index = 1 to N
         INPUT #7: List(Index)
      NEXT Index
   END SUB !FillArray

   SUB WriteArray (List(), Nmbr, #10)
   ! Write an array of Nmbr numbers to a file.
      FOR Index = 1 to Nmbr
         PRINT #10: List(Index)
      NEXT Index
      CLOSE #10
   END SUB !WriteArray
```

The following output is produced by this program:

```
Name of input file? SORT-IN.DAT
Name of output file? SORT-OUT.DAT


Unsorted:
  123   65  887    3    0  110    7   -6

Sorted:
   -6    0    3    7   65  110  123  887

The sorted list is in the output file.
```

A call to the subroutine `DisplayArray` is inserted in the program before and after the `BubbleSort` subroutine is called. These two procedure calls display the list before and after sorting and would probably be deleted in a production version of the program. Note that subroutine `FillArray` must read through the file twice, once to count the numbers in the file and redimension the array, then a second time to assign each numeric value to an array element.

Before reading the file a second time, a `RESET` statement is used to move the file pointer to the beginning of the input file. Another alternative is to close and then reopen the file but that takes longer and is more complicated. After the numbers in the file have been counted, the array `List` is redimensioned to hold the entire list of numbers.

TIP: It is not possible to sort a text file directly because there is no way to access individual lines in the file. Remember, you cannot jump from place to place and read individual lines. Some other types of files can be sorted directly.

You probably noticed that I used different variable names – `Count`, `N`, and `NumOfItems` – for the number of items in the list. Sometimes I had to use a short name like `N` to prevent a statement from becoming too long for the book page. At other times, I used different names to show you it makes no difference, an argument and its corresponding parameter have to agree in position and type but not in name. If you don't understand, go back and read the discussion in Chapter 8 again.

This program, as written, is limited only by the amount of memory available for storing the array. Most small computers do not have enough memory to hold very large arrays in memory. More sophisticated sorting algorithms have been developed that allow large disk files – but not text files – to be sorted quickly and efficiently.

Challenge Problem 9-2

When using the bubble sort algorithm, you may have noticed that after the first scan through the list is completed, the largest number has moved to the right end of the list. Each successive scan moves the next largest number toward the right end, leaving a shorter list of numbers that actually needs to be scanned the next time. On the basis of these observations, can you write a modified bubble sort procedure that sorts a list more quickly?

HINT: In the preceding Challenge Problem, make the final limit value of the `FOR` loop (now `N - 1`) a variable that gets smaller as each scan is completed.

9.4 BRIDGE INSPECTION, Part IV

Let's go back to the bridge inspection program and add another command to the menu. I want to do some preliminary design work with you and discuss one or two new ideas, but I want you to do most of the programming work.

If you look back at Example Program 8-4, you see that one menu choice calculates the average measured frequency for a specified bridge. You should have no problem writing a procedure that calculates the average frequency for each one of the 23 bridges. This is a suggested program for Challenge Problem 8-3.

If you thought about putting the 23 total scores in an array then we are on the same wavelength. What kind of array? A one-dimensional array? A two-dimensional array? That's a hard question to answer at this point, isn't it? Remember, don't try to develop a solution until you understand the problem!

Challenge Problem 9-3

The problem is to add another item of choice to the menu. This menu choice should display a two-column list of bridge names, not numbers, and the natural frequency for each bridge. The list should appear in alphabetic order by bridge name. The list would be useful for any maintenance engineer who wanted to look up a particular bridge's frequency.

It is absolutely necessary that you know which bridge name is associated with which frequency as you interchange items while sorting a list of bridge names. In other words, the identity of the bridge has to remain with the frequency. One of the best ways to accomplish this task is to use a two-dimensional array, one column containing bridge names and the other containing bridge frequencies. When you move a name, you must also move the corresponding frequency. The two always stay together; that is, you move the array row. Doesn't that make sense?

You need one more item of information to complete your program, a list of bridge names and numbers. The file NAMES.DAT provides that list. It contains 23 names, starting with Mormon River. The position in the list is each bridge's number. This file is on the same disk as the file FREQS.DAT.

9.5 PROGRAMS THAT MODIFY TEXT FILES

I now discuss another type of program, one that changes the format of a text file. Sometimes a text file of information – for example, test results – is in the wrong format to be read by a program that analyses that information. Assume you have such a data file whose lines are in the following format:

```
emission test/1995/0.013 percent
```

The analysis program available for your use requires that lines of input data be in a different format, as shown:

```
"emission test","1995","0.013 percent"
```

A conversion program in True BASIC to produce a new data file in the correct format is quite simple and easy to write. An outline of the program might look as follows:

- Ask for the file or path names of both input and output files and open these files.
- Read the first line from the input file
- Using string functions, replace each slash with a comma and place quotation marks around the substrings —the strings between commas
- Write the modified line of text on the output file
- Continue the process until all the lines have been read, modified, and written

Challenge Problem 9-4

The problem is as stated in the preceding section. Every item in each line of the file is now separated from adjoining items by slashes and these slashes must be changed to commas. Furthermore, every item must be enclosed in quotation marks. In database language, the line of text is usually called a *record* and each separated item in the line is called a *field*.

Consider how you might modify one line from the input file. You might use the `Pos` function or one of its derivatives to find the locations of all the slashes in that line. You then might consider replacing every slash by a three-character group consisting of a quotation mark, a comma, and another quotation mark. Finally, you would need to put a quotation mark at the beginning of the line and at the end of the line.

Having converted one line, you know how to convert all lines. Your program must also open and close files and read and write information.

When you have finished the program, create a test file and let your program modify the test file's format. That is the only way to learn for certain if your program is working properly. You should try files of different lengths containing different fields.

You might also try running your program with a file that has an error in it. After all, even database files can contain errors, no matter how carefully the data is entered. Think about what information you would need to know in order to catch errors and how that part of your program might work. Can your program handle a line with the error shown?

```
emission test//1995/0.013 percent
```

How about this error?

```
/emission test/1995/0.013 percent/
```

On the other hand, there is no way you can detect an error in the following line without knowing the context of the line – it actually isn't an error if you ignore the context:

```
emission test/1995 0.013 percent
```

Above all, remember what I said many chapters ago about testing. A program is not finished until it is thoroughly tested!

What You Have Learned

I certainly haven't covered all the capabilities of True BASIC, but the information you have learned should let you write significant programs. I know many engineers who use True BASIC exclusively for writing computer programs.

I hope this chapter gives you a boost in the right direction and increases your confidence in your ability to write longer programs. You can continue to learn computer programming by writing more programs.

Good luck in your future computer programming endeavors.

Topic	Page
A technique for measuring program execution time	115
Differences in the speed of calculations	116
Error trapping and handling	119
Using a binary flag	121
The bubble-sort algorithm	122
Passing channel numbers as parameters	125
A general file-sorting program	126
Sorting a two-dimensional array	129
Conversion programs to modify data files	130

Figure 9.2*—What you have learned in Chapter 9.*

★

APPENDICES

Computer Access

If you already own a personal computer or have access to one, you can skip this appendix. If not, read on.

COMPUTER AVAILABILITY

As you read this book, it is important that you either own a personal computer or have access to one. I am firmly convinced that you can learn a computer language only while you have an opportunity to practice writing programs on a computer. This book is designed to be read while sitting in front of a computer with your hands on the keyboard.

If you don't own a computer and can't buy one right now, there are other possibilities. Many schools and colleges have public computer rooms for student use. You may be able to get permission from a local school to use their computer facilities after school hours. Public libraries are another place where computers may be available that you can use. If there are computer stores in your area, talk to them about your problem. They may be willing to lease or loan you a new or used computer at a reasonable cost.

BUYING A COMPUTER SYSTEM

As a former college professor teaching introductory computer courses, I have been asked for advice on buying a computer system by literally thousands of students. Here are some ideas and recommendations:

Choosing a Computer

The market is dominated by two general classifications of computers. One is the IBM PC and its many clones, collectively called DOS or Windows machines; the other is the Apple Macintosh. True BASIC is available for both types of machines. How do you make a choice?

There is probably a greater variety of software available for DOS machines. Many people like the Macintosh because its operating system is strongly graphics oriented and simple to use. With the continuing development of Windows by Microsoft, DOS computers are becoming more and more like Macintosh computers. If you can, try out both types of computers and make your choice. If you can't decide, I recommend a DOS computer with Windows because it is by far the most popular machine today. If you asked me for my personal preference, however, I would tell you that I find the Macintosh much easier and more pleasant to use.

The next question is whether to get a desktop or a laptop machine. The laptop is portable but more expensive than a desktop with similar capabilities. The desktop machine costs less to expand — to add a second fixed disk or a CD-ROM player. Unless portability is important, buy a desktop computer.

As I have already mentioned, the speed of a computer's CPU is important. If you use your machine primarily for programming and maybe word processing, you don't need the highest speed. On the other hand, a slow machine can be annoying. My advice is to buy the fastest machine you can afford. You'll never regret buying a computer that's too fast – you may regret buying one that's too slow.

Ample memory and disk space are important as application programs get bigger and bigger each year. Memory prices fluctuate over a wide range, if they are not at a high peak when you buy your computer, have at least 16 megabytes installed. In any case, don't buy less than 8 megabytes. I think a one gigabyte or 1000 megabyte fixed or hard disk is a good choice, it should provide plenty of space unless you plan to save lots of graphic images. On a desktop machine, it is usually easy to add a second fixed disk at any time. On a laptop this is difficult, so get the largest fixed disk offered for your laptop.

An interesting comment about disk drives: A year ago I was advising 500 megabytes but prices have been falling so fast that now the same amount of money will buy 1000 megabytes. This latter capacity should satisfy your needs for several years.

TIP: If you purchase a one gigabyte or larger disk and plan to save lots of short True BASIC programs on it, ask a computer expert to show you how to partition your hard disk. You can avoid wasting a lot of disk space when saving small files by dividing a large hard disk into a number of smaller partitions.

I cannot give you specific advice on choice of keyboard and monitor because so much depends on your personal preferences. Try out a keyboard before you buy it. Different models have different key actions — some soft and mushy, some hard and "clicky." You should pick the one that feels best to you.

You will spend a lot of time looking at your monitor so make sure you like what you see. On a desktop computer, my personal choice would be a color monitor with a 17-inch screen. Most of the new applications use colors to good advantage. I like the larger screen for word processing because it makes such tasks as page layout easier. You may be well satisfied, however, with a more common and considerably less expensive 15-inch monitor. On a laptop, be sure to look at the screen under different lighting conditions before making your choice. If you can afford it, I recommend an “active matrix LCD screen.”

The ability to access a network is rapidly becoming a requirement for many personal computers. Probably the most widely used network is the Internet. A program named Network Navigator allows you to browse through the Internet and its World Wide Web, as well as receive and send electronic mail. If you are at an institution that provides network connections in your office or dormitory room, ask a local computer expert what equipment you need to access that network. If you must connect to the Internet through the telephone system, you should purchase a device called a modem. Once again, high speed is important – you should get a modem that operates at 28,800 bits per second or faster.

Finally, you need to consider the questions of service availability and an adequate warranty. Almost all vendors, even mail order vendors, offer a one-year warranty. Many offer a three-year warranty and on-site — that means in your home or office — repair service for the first year. When I bought my IBM laptop computer, I received a three-year warranty and was thankful for it when I had to replace the screen in the second year.

Selecting Software

Your computer should come with the fixed disk formatted and an operating system installed. I recommend that you ask for the latest version of Windows which at this writing is Windows 95 – it has the MS-DOS operating system built into it. You don’t have to make a choice on a Macintosh, you should receive the latest version of the MacOS system. Other software may be bundled with your computer – if you want that particular software, fine, but don’t pay extra for software you don’t want and may never use.

The first software package I would recommend is a utilities package — my own favorite is the Norton Utilities. I find two programs in this package essential. One program (Disk Doctor) checks the condition of your fixed disk, reports any problems it finds, and in almost every case, is able to repair the problem. Keeping your fixed disk in good shape prevents serious problems from developing. The second utility program (Unerase) recovers a file that you have erased by mistake. Recovery of an erased file can save you a lot of time and effort.

If you are learning True BASIC, you need a copy of the True BASIC language system. I recommend the latest version of the Student Edition. As I write, this edition costs about $20 and that includes an excellent manual. You can't beat the quality or the price! Here is the mailing address:

True BASIC, Inc..
12 Commerce Avenue
West Lebanon, NH 03784

You can also reach True BASIC by:

Phone:	Fax:	E-Mail
603 298-8517	603 298-7015	sales@truebasic.com http://www.truebasic.com

Probably the most-widely-used program on personal computers is a word processor. The two leaders are Microsoft Word and Word Perfect. Before making your purchase, get information on these two and other word processors, arrange for a demonstration if possible, and make your choice. The selection of a word processor depends almost entirely on personal preference.

The next-most-widely-used program is a spreadsheet. If much of your work is financial in nature, a spreadsheet may be your most important program. There are three leaders to choose from: Lotus 1-2-3, Microsoft Excel, and Quattro Pro. They are all good programs and the choice is again a matter of personal preference.

An attractive alternative to separate word processing and spreadsheet software is a combination software package. The best of these is Claris Works (currently version 4.0) for either Macintosh or Windows 95. Word processing, spreadsheet, database, drawing, painting, and presentation applications are completely integrated in one program. I think you will be impressed by the quality and capability of each of Claris Works' applications. An added advantage is that it sells for a fraction of the price of either Microsoft Word or Microsoft Excel, so Claris Works is a good choice if you are not yet sure what word processor or spreadsheet to buy..

Finally, you need a network browser if you plan to connect your computer to the Internet. I recommend Network Navigator (version 2.0 or higher). Your institution or a local computer store should be able to tell you how to obtain a copy of this software at no cost or for a very low price. You will almost certainly need help or detailed instructions when making your initial connection to the Internet.

Starting True BASIC

This appendix explains how to start True BASIC on two popular types of computers – an IBM-compatible running DOS or Windows and an Apple Macintosh running MacOS. The main problem is making sure that True BASIC knows where to find all required information.

IBM-Compatible

If you are running under DOS, you must make sure that your current directory is the directory containing True BASIC. If that directory is named TRUE and is on disk C, for example, you can make this directory your current directory by entering the following command after the DOS prompt:

```
C:\> CD C:\TRUE\
```

The command CD means "change directory" and the DOS prompt is changed. Now enter the command HELLO after the new DOS prompt and the True BASIC program will start. Here is what you should see on your screen:

```
C:\TRUE> HELLO
```

The italic face is just my convention for showing that the commands CD and HELLO are typed in by you, the user.

If you are running under Windows with a version of True BASIC prior to Version 5, you can leave Windows, go into DOS, and carry out the preceding steps. Alternately, whoever installed True BASIC on your computer may have created an icon for the True BASIC program. You can then start by clicking on that icon. If the installation was done properly, the True BASIC program will begin.

A problem arises when you try to access one of the auxiliary programs like the help file in directory TBHELP. Unless you take further steps, the True BASIC program will not know where to find this file. The solution is to place a startup file in the same directory as True BASIC, in this case, directory TRUE. That startup file must be named STARTUP.TRU and you can create it with the True BASIC editor. At a minimum, it should contain the following three statements:

```
ALIAS help, "", "C:\TRUE\TBHELP\"
ALIAS do, "", "C:\TRUE\TBDO\"
ALIAS library, "", "C:\TRUE\TBLIBS\"
```

The ALIAS command tells the computer where to look for information. For example, it should look for the help file first in the current directory ("") and if not there, then in the subdirectory TBHELP of the directory TRUE on the disk in drive C. If you have the Student Edition of True BASIC, look in Appendix E of its manual for more information.

Apple Macintosh

Starting True BASIC on a Macintosh is relatively easy. Look for the True BASIC icon, maybe on the desktop, maybe in the True BASIC folder wherever that may be. I keep the True BASIC folder in the fixed disk folder on my desktop and every component of the True BASIC system is stored in that folder. The programs I write, however, are kept in a completely different set of folders. I also keep an alias of the True BASIC icon on the edge of the desktop where it is always in view and available.

Once you have found the True BASIC icon or its alias, double-click on it and the program starts, displaying only the editing window. You can write a new program in that window and when you are finished, execute it by selecting the Run command from the Run menu.

True BASIC Medalist Series

The 1996-1997 period will see the release of new Bronze, Silver, and Gold editions of True BASIC which include many new interface-building commands. These new editions often show two icons. To start writing your program you would double-click on the one for the editor. An editing window is opened in which you can write your program. The procedure for executing a program is similar for MS-DOS, Windows, and MacOS – select the Run command from the Run menu.

Reserved Words

The following words **cannot** be uses as the name of numeric variables, functions, or subroutines.

ELSE NOT PRINT REM

The following words **cannot** be uses as the name of numeric variables, arrays, or functions.

CON DATE EXLINE EXTYPE IDN MAXNUM PI RND RUN-TIME TIME ZER

The following words **cannot** be uses as the name of string variables, arrays, or functions.

DATE$ EXLINE$ EXTEXT$ TIME$ NUL$

Numeric Formats

Exponential Notation

Numbers may be written or displayed in decimal format such as 13.375 or in exponential format. The latter format is especially useful for very large or very small numbers. For example, the number 1,475,000,000,000 can be written as 1.475e+12 or 1.475E+12. This format is shorthand notation for 1.475 multiplied by 10 raised to the 12th power (or 1.475 multiplied by a number consisting of a one followed by 12 zeroes). The plus sign is optional — the number can also be written as 1.475E12. Small numbers can be displayed in a similar fashion, the number .0000228 being written as 2.28E-5 which is 2.28 divided by 10 raised to the 5th power.

Depending on the size of a number, True BASIC will make an automatic choice to display the number in either decimal or exponential format. When you use a number in a program, as a constant, or as the value of a variable, you can write it in either format. A user can enter a number in response to the `INPUT` statement in either format. The following paragraphs explain how True BASIC selects a numeric format for display.

Default Numeric Formats

True BASIC has a built-in set of formatting rules for displaying numbers. In most cases, numbers are displayed in an appropriate format with no special effort on your part.

Positive numbers and zero are displayed with a leading space. Negative numbers are displayed with a leading minus sign. All numbers end with a trailing space, even if followed by a semicolon in a `PRINT` statement.

If a number can be represented as an integer (whole number) with eight or fewer digits, it is displayed in integer format.

```
PRINT (7) displays  7
PRINT (1725) displays  1725
PRINT (-12345678) displays -12345678
```

If a number can be represented by eight or fewer digits preceding a decimal point, it is displayed in decimal format. Digits following the decimal point are rounded so that the total number of digits displayed does not exceed eight. Trailing zeroes after the decimal point and leading zeroes before the decimal point are not displayed.

```
PRINT (1.4) displays  1.4
PRINT (12345.6789) displays  12345.679
PRINT (-70410000.57) displays -70410001.
PRINT (0.00000006) displays  .00000006
```

In all other cases, a number is displayed in exponential format, with eight or fewer digits in that part of the number before the letter "E." Trailing zeroes after the decimal point are not displayed. Leading zeroes are not displayed, the leading digit must be between one and nine.

```
PRINT (123456789123456789) displays  1.2345679e+17
PRINT (0.0000000654321) displays  6.54321E-8
```

The letter "E" can be either uppercase or lowercase, as shown in the preceding examples.

True BASIC rounds numbers to eight significant figures, if necessary, before displaying them in exponential notation. For greater display precision, you can use the `PRINT USING` statement. Remember that True BASIC always maintains an internal precision of 14 to 16 significant figures for all numbers.

Dollar Amounts with Commas

Sometimes you need to display a dollar amount with a leading dollar sign and commas separating every three digits. There is no straightforward way to create this format in True BASIC so you have to use a couple of tricks. The following program illustrates one method of creating the desired format:

```
! Example Program D-1
! Display a left-justified number
! with a leading dollar sign.

INPUT prompt "Value? ": Value
LET F$ = "###,###,###.##"
LET Value$ = "$" & Trim$(Using$(F$, Value))
PRINT Value$
END
```

The user is prompted to enter a number. The function `Using$` converts the number `Value` to a formatted string and the function `Trim$` removes any leading or trailing blanks. A dollar sign is appended to the beginning of the string and it is assigned to the variable `Value$`. Here are two program runs:

```
Value? 123.45
$123.45

Value? 123456.789
$123,456.79
```

Built-In Functions

1. ARITHMETIC FUNCTIONS

ABS(X)
returns the absolute value of X

CEIL(X)
returns the least integer that is greater than or equal to X, equivalent to -Int(-X)

DIVIDE(X, Y, Q, R)
a subroutine that divides X by Y, and returns the quotient Q and the remainder R

EPS(X)
returns the smallest number that can be added to X such that the result differs from X

EXP(X)
returns the exponential function of X

FP(X)
returns the fractional part of X

INT(X)
returns the greatest integer less than or equal to X

IP(X)
returns the integer part of X

LOG(X)
returns the natural logarithm of X

LOG2(X)
returns the logarithm of X to the base 2

LOG10(X)
returns the logarithm of X to the base 10

MAX(X,Y)
returns the maximum value of X and Y

MAXNUM
returns the largest positive number in True BASIC (see Appendix A)

MIN(X,Y)
returns the minimum value of X and Y

MOD(X,Y)
returns X modulo Y, equivalent to (X - (Y * Int(X/Y)))

REMAINDER(X,Y)
returns the remainder left after dividing X by Y

RND
returns a random number in the range 0 <= Rnd < 1

ROUND(X)
returns X rounded to an integer

ROUND(X, N)
returns X rounded to N decimal places

SGN(X)
returns a value of 1 if X > 0, 0 if X = 0, -1 if X < 0

SQR(X)
returns the square root of X

TRUNCATE(X, N)
returns X truncated to N decimal places

2. TRIGONOMETRIC FUNCTIONS

ACOS(X)
returns the arccosine of X

ANGLE(X, Y)
returns counterclockwise angle between the X axis and a line from the origin to point (X, Y)

ASIN(X)
returns the arcsine of X

ATN(X)
returns the arctangent of X

COS(X)
returns the cosine of angle X

COSH(X)
returns the hyperbolic cosine of angle X

COT(X)
returns the cotangent of angle X

CSC(X)
returns the cosecant of angle X

DEG(X)
converts an angle of X radians to degrees

PI
returns the value of π (equal to 3.14159...)

RAD(X)
converts an angle of X degrees to radians

SEC(X)
returns the secant of angle X

SIN(X)
returns the sine of angle X

SINH(X)
returns the hyperbolic sine of angle X

TAN(X)
returns the tangent of angle X

TANH(X)
returns the hyperbolic tangent of angle X

3. STRING FUNCTIONS

CHR$(N)
returns a character corresponding to the ASCII value N

CPOS(A$, B$, N)
returns the position of the first occurrence of any character of B$ that is in A$, starting at character N in A$ and searching right

CPOSR(A$, B$, N)
returns the position of the last occurrence of any character of B$ that is in A$, starting at character N in A$ and searching left

LEN(A$)
returns the length of string A$ measured in characters

LCASE$(A$)
changes any uppercase characters in A$ to lowercase

LTRIM$(A$)
trims all leading spaces from A$

MAXLEN(A$)
returns the maximum length of the string variable A$

NCPOS(A$, B$, N)
returns the position of the first occurrence of any character of B$ that is not in A$, starting at character N in A$ and searching right

NCPOSR(A$, B$, N)
returns the position of the last occurrence of any character of B$ that is not in A$, starting at character N in A$ and searching left

NUM(A$)
reverses the action of NUM$(N) by restoring the numeric value stored in the string A$

NUM$(N)
converts a number N to an internal string representation that cannot be displayed

ORD(A$)
returns the ASCII value of the first character in A$

POS(A$, B$)
returns the position of the first occurrence of B$ in A$

POS(A$, B$, N)
returns the position of the first occurrence of B$ in A$, starting at character N in A$ and searching right

POSR(A$, B$, N)
returns the position of the last occurrence of B$ in A$, starting at character N in A$ and searching left

REPEAT$(A$, N)
returns a string containing A$ repeated N times

RTRIM$(A$)
trims all trailing spaces from A$

STR$(N)
converts a number N to a string

TRIM$(A$)
trims all leading and trailing spaces from A$

UCASE$(A$)
changes any lowercase characters in A$ to uppercase

USING$(F$, V1, V2...)
returns a string containing variables V1, V2,... formatted by F$

VAL(A$)
converts string A$ to a number

4. DATE and TIME FUNCTIONS

DATE
returns the current date in YYDDD format, where DDD is the day of the year and YY is the year of the century

TIME
returns the current time measured in seconds since midnight

DATE$
returns the current date in YYYYMMDD format

TIME$
returns the current time in HH:MM:SS format

5. ARRAY and MATRIX FUNCTIONS

CON
returns a numeric array whose elements are all one, as in program statement MAT(A) = CON

DET(A)
returns the determinant of the numeric array A

DOT(A, B)
returns the dot product of the one-dimensional numeric arrays A and B

IDN
returns a square numeric array that is an identity matrix, as in statement MAT(A) = IDN

INV(A)
returns the inverse of the square numeric array A

LBOUND(A, N)
returns the lower bound in dimension N of array A

NUL$
returns a string array whose elements are all null strings, as in statement MAT(A$) = NUL$

SIZE(A, N)
returns the number of elements in dimension N of array A

TRN(A)
returns the transpose of the numeric array A

UBOUND(A, N)
returns the upper bound in dimension N of array A

ZER
returns a numeric array all of whose elements are zeroes, as in the statement MAT(A) = ZER

6. MISCELLANEOUS FUNCTIONS

EXLINE
returns the line number in a program where the most recent error occurred

EXLINE$
returns a string giving the location in a program where the most recent error occurred

EXTEXT$
returns the error message associated with the most recent error trapped by an error handler

EXTYPE
returns the error number of the most recent error trapped by an error handler

PEEK(addr)
returns a number that is the contents of the memory address in bytes given by addr

POKE(addr, value)
a subroutine that accesses memory location addr and changes its contents to value

TAB(N)
moves the printing cursor in a PRINT statement to column N

TAB(R, C)
moves the printing cursor in a PRINT statement to row R and column C, the printing equivalent of the SET CURSOR R, C statement

APPENDIX F

ASCII Codes

Name	Num
ctrl-@ (null)	0
ctrl-A	1
ctrl-B	2
ctrl-C (break)	3
ctrl-D	4
ctrl-E	5
ctrl-F	6
ctrl-G (bell)	7
ctrl-H (backspace)	8
ctrl-I (tab)	9
ctrl-J (line feed)	10
ctrl-K	11
ctrl-L (form feed)	12
ctrl-M (return)	13
ctrl-N	14
ctrl-O	15
ctrl-P	16
ctrl-Q	17
ctrl-R	18
ctrl-S	19
ctrl-T	20
ctrl-U	21
ctrl-V	22
ctrl-W	23
ctrl-X	24
ctrl-Y	25
ctrl-Z (end of file)	26
ctrl-[(escape)	27
ctrl-\	28
ctrl-]	29
ctrl-^	30
ctrl-_	31
sp (space)	32
!	33
"	34
#	35
$	36
%	37
& (ampersand)	38
' (acute accent) (also single quote)	39
(	40
)	41
*	42
+	43
, (comma)	44
- (minus)	45
. (period)	46
/ (forward slash)	47
0 (zero)	48
1	49
2	50
3	51
4	52
5	53
6	54
7	55
8	56
9	57
:	58

<table>
<tr><th>Name</th><th>Num</th></tr>
<tr><td>;</td><td>59</td></tr>
<tr><td><</td><td>60</td></tr>
<tr><td></td><td>61</td></tr>
<tr><td>></td><td>62</td></tr>
<tr><td>?</td><td>63</td></tr>
<tr><td>@</td><td>64</td></tr>
<tr><td>A (uppercase)</td><td>65</td></tr>
<tr><td>B</td><td>66</td></tr>
<tr><td>C</td><td>67</td></tr>
<tr><td>D</td><td>68</td></tr>
<tr><td>E</td><td>69</td></tr>
<tr><td>F</td><td>70</td></tr>
<tr><td>G</td><td>71</td></tr>
<tr><td>H</td><td>72</td></tr>
<tr><td>I</td><td>73</td></tr>
<tr><td>J</td><td>74</td></tr>
<tr><td>K</td><td>75</td></tr>
<tr><td>L</td><td>76</td></tr>
<tr><td>M</td><td>77</td></tr>
<tr><td>N</td><td>78</td></tr>
<tr><td>O</td><td>79</td></tr>
<tr><td>P</td><td>80</td></tr>
<tr><td>Q</td><td>81</td></tr>
<tr><td>R</td><td>82</td></tr>
<tr><td>S</td><td>83</td></tr>
<tr><td>T</td><td>84</td></tr>
<tr><td>U</td><td>85</td></tr>
<tr><td>V</td><td>86</td></tr>
<tr><td>W</td><td>87</td></tr>
<tr><td>X</td><td>88</td></tr>
<tr><td>Y</td><td>89</td></tr>
<tr><td>Z</td><td>90</td></tr>
<tr><td>[(left bracket)</td><td>91</td></tr>
<tr><td>\ (backslash)</td><td>92</td></tr>
<tr><td>] (right bracket)</td><td>93</td></tr>
<tr><td>^ (caret)</td><td>94</td></tr>
<tr><td>_ (underline)</td><td>95</td></tr>
<tr><td>` (grave accent)</td><td>96</td></tr>
<tr><td>a (lowercase)</td><td>97</td></tr>
<tr><td>b</td><td>98</td></tr>
<tr><td>c</td><td>99</td></tr>
<tr><td>d</td><td>100</td></tr>
<tr><td>e</td><td>101</td></tr>
<tr><td>f</td><td>102</td></tr>
<tr><td>g</td><td>103</td></tr>
<tr><td>h</td><td>104</td></tr>
<tr><td>i</td><td>105</td></tr>
<tr><td>j</td><td>106</td></tr>
<tr><td>k</td><td>107</td></tr>
<tr><td>l</td><td>108</td></tr>
<tr><td>m</td><td>109</td></tr>
<tr><td>n</td><td>110</td></tr>
<tr><td>o</td><td>111</td></tr>
<tr><td>p</td><td>112</td></tr>
<tr><td>q</td><td>113</td></tr>
<tr><td>r</td><td>114</td></tr>
<tr><td>s</td><td>115</td></tr>
<tr><td>t</td><td>116</td></tr>
<tr><td>u</td><td>117</td></tr>
<tr><td>v</td><td>118</td></tr>
<tr><td>w</td><td>119</td></tr>
<tr><td>x</td><td>120</td></tr>
<tr><td>y</td><td>121</td></tr>
<tr><td>z</td><td>122</td></tr>
<tr><td>{ (left brace)</td><td>123</td></tr>
<tr><td>| (vertical bar)</td><td>124</td></tr>
<tr><td>} (right brace)</td><td>125</td></tr>
<tr><td>~ (tilde)</td><td>126</td></tr>
<tr><td>del (delete)</td><td>127</td></tr>
</table>

All characters are displayed in the Courier typeface.

Run-Time Errors Messages

Extype	Extext$
1000	Overflow in numeric constant.
1002	Overflow.
1003	Overflow in numeric function.
1004	Overflow in VAL.
1005	Overflow in MAT operation.
1006	Overflow in READ.
1007	Overflow in INPUT (nonfatal).
1008	Overflow in file INPUT.
1009	Overflow in DET or DOT.
1051	String too long.
1052	String too long in MAT.
1053	String too long in READ.
1054	String too long in INPUT (nonfatal).
1105	String too long in file INPUT.
1106	String too long in assignment.
2001	Subscript out of bounds.
3001	Division by zero.
3002	Negative number to non–integral power.
3003	Zero to negative power.
3004	LOG of number <= 0.
3005	SQR of negative number.
3006	MOD and REMAINDER can't have 0 as 2nd argument.
3007	ASIN and ACOS argument must be between 1 and –1.
3008	Can't use ANGLE(0,0).
3009	Can't invert singular matrix.
–3050	Argument for SIN, COS, or TAN too large.
–3051	Argument too large or small for accurate result.
4001	VAL string isn't a proper number.
4002	CHR$ argument must be between 0 and 255.
4003	Improper ORD string.
4004	SIZE index out of range.

Extype	Extext$
4005	TAB column less than 1 (nonfatal).
4006	MARGIN less than zonewidth.
4007	ZONEWIDTH out of range.
4008	LBOUND index out of range.
4009	UBOUND index out of range.
4010	REPEAT$ count < 0.
–4020	Improper NUM string.
4102	Improper TEXT JUSTIFY value (nonfatal).
4301	Mismatched parameters for CHAIN/PROGRAM.
4302	Mismatched dimensions for CHAIN/PROGRAM.
–4501	Error in PLAY string.
5000	Out of memory.
5001	Array too large.
6001	Mismatched array sizes.
6002	DET needs a square matrix.
6003	INV needs a square matrix.
6004	IDN must make a square matrix.
6005	Illegal array bounds.
7001	Channel number must be 1 to 1000.
7002	Can't use #0 here (nonfatal).
7003	Channel is already open.
7004	Channel isn't open.
7051	Record LENGTH <= 0.
7100	Unknown value for OPEN option.
7102	Too many channels open.
7103	File's record size doesn't match OPEN RECSIZE.
7104	Wrong type of file.
7202	Must be RECORD or BYTE for SET RECORD.
7204	Can't use SAME here.
–7250	Can't SET RECSIZE on non–empty RECORD file.
–7251	Must be BYTE file or empty for SET RECSIZE.
–7252	File pointer out of bounds.
7301	Can't ERASE file not opened as OUTIN.
7302	Can't output to INPUT file.
7303	Can't input from OUTPUT file.
7308	Can't PRINT or WRITE to middle of this file.
7312	Can't set ZONEWIDTH or MARGIN for this file.
7313	Can't set ZONEWIDTH or MARGIN for INPUT file.

Extype	Extext$
7317	Can't PRINT to INTERNAL file.
7318	Can't INPUT from INTERNAL file.
7321	Can't SKIP REST on STREAM file.
–7351	Must be BYTE file for READ BYTES.
7401	Channel is not open for TRACE.
7402	Wrong file type for TRACE.
8001	Reading past end of data.
8002	Too few input items (nonfatal).
8003	Too many input items (nonfatal).
8011	Reading past end of file.
8012	Too few data in record.
8013	Too many data in record.
8101	Data item isn't a number.
8102	Badly formed input line (nonfatal).
8103	String given instead of number (nonfatal).
–8104	Data item isn't a string.
8105	Badly formed input line from file.
8201	Badly formed USING string.
8202	No USING item for output.
8203	USING value too large for field (nonfatal).
8208	USING exponent too large for field (nonfatal).
8301	Output item bigger than RECSIZE.
8302	Input item bigger than RECSIZE.
–8304	Must SET RECSIZE before WRITE.
8401	Input timeout.
8402	Timeout value < 0.
–8450	Nested INPUT statements with TIMEOUT clauses.
–8501	Must be TEXT file.
–8502	Must be RECORD or BYTE file.
–8503	Can't use READ or WRITE for TEXT file.
9000	File I/O error.
9001	File is read or write protected.
9002	Trouble using disk or printer.
9003	No such file.
9004	File already exists.
9005	Diskette removed, or wrong diskette.
9006	Disk full.
9007	Too many channels open.

Extype	Extext$
9008	No such directory.
9100	Can't open temporary file.
9101	Can't open PRINTER.
9601	Cursor set out of bounds.
10001	ON index out of range, no ELSE given.
10002	RETURN without GOSUB.
10004	No CASE selected, but no CASE ELSE.
10005	Program not available for CHAIN.
–10006	Exception in CHAINed program.
10007	Break statement encountered.
11000	Can't do graphics on this computer.
–11001	Window minimum = maximum.
–11002	Screen minimum >= maximum.
–11003	Screen bounds must be 0 to 1.
11004	Can't SET WINDOW in picture.
–11005	Channel isn't a window.
–11008	No such color.
11140	No GET MOUSE on this computer

MAT Statements

This appendix assumes that you have read Chapter 3 and have some experience with matrices. If not, first read about matrices in a good mathematics textbook such as Thomas and Finney, *Calculus and Analytic Geometry.*

Matrix is a mathematician's name for an array of numbers. Simple operations with matrices include addition, subtraction, multiplication, and inversion — the equivalent of division. Matrix equations are written using these operations. A group of MAT statements in True BASIC allow you to manipulate matrices, as shown in the following example programs.

Matrix Input and Output

To use matrices in a program, you must first assign element values to them. You can assign values in a simple program with nested FOR loops but there is a better alternative — use MAT statements. Here is an example program that uses the MAT READ and MAT PRINT statements to read values from a memory data file and display them on the screen:

```
! Example Program H-1
! Assign values to two matrices.

DIM A(1:3, 1:3), B(1:3, 1:3)
MAT READ A, B
PRINT "Matrix A"
MAT PRINT A;
PRINT "Matrix B"
MAT PRINT B;

DATA 2,3,7,5,1,2,6,2,3
DATA 3,9,1,7,8,7,2,1,5
END
```

The MAT READ assigns values to one or more matrices. Values are read by row, sometimes called "in odometer order" meaning that the last index changes the fastest. You can also assign values from a file using the MAT INPUT # statement. A trailing semicolon after each MAT PRINT statement displays the matrices in compact form. See for yourself what happens when you leave off that semicolon. Here are the results of Example Program H-1:

```
Matrix A
 2  3  7
 5  1  2
 6  2  3

Matrix B
 3  9  1
 7  8  7
 2  1  5
```

Because matrix arrays all have a lower-bound index value of 1, you can use the short notation for matrix dimensions. The following program fragment shows how the element values of one matrix are assigned to another matrix:

```
DIM C(3,3), A(3,3)
MAT C = A
```

Note that the word `LET` is not part of the matrix assignment statement. Matrix C should be the same size as matrix A. I say "should" instead of "must" because it is possible to redimension a matrix with the assignment statement. My advice, however, is to avoid that feature — it can be confusing. Always dimension the two matrices in an assignment statement to the same size.

Matrix Addition and Subtraction

You can add or subtract two matrices by adding or subtracting the values of their respective elements. The two matrices and the resulting matrix should all be of the same size — that is, have the same number of dimensions, rows, and columns. These operations are demonstrated in the following program:

```
! Example Program H-2
! Assign values to two matrices,
! then display their sum and difference.

DIM A(3,3), B(3,3), C(3,3)
MAT READ A, B
MAT C = A + B
PRINT "Matrix A + Matrix B"
MAT PRINT C;
MAT C = A - B
PRINT "Matrix A - Matrix B"
MAT PRINT C;

DATA 2,3,7,5,1,2,6,2,3
DATA 3,9,1,7,8,7,2,1,5
END
```

In the following display of program output, element spacing in the first matrix is not quite as uniform as in the second — some element values have two digits.

Matrices A and B have the same values as in Example H-1.

```
Matrix A + Matrix B
 5  12  8
 12  9  9
 6  3  8

Matrix A - Matrix B
-1 -6 -6
-2 -7 -5
 4  1 -2
```

Matrix Multiplication

Multiplication of two matrices is only defined when the number of columns in the first matrix is equal to the number of rows in the second matrix. The two matrices do not have to be the same size. Furthermore, the order of multiplication is significant — matrix multiplication is said to be *non-commutative*. If both A (B and B (A can be calculated, they normally have different values. Here is a program that shows how to multiply two matrices:

```
! Example Program H-3
! Assign values to two matrices,
! then display their product.

DIM A(3, 3), B(3, 3), C(3, 3)
MAT READ A, B
MAT C = A * B
PRINT "Matrix A x Matrix B"
MAT PRINT C;
MAT C = B * A
PRINT "Matrix B x Matrix A"
MAT PRINT C;

DATA 2,3,7,5,1,2,6,2,3
DATA 3,9,1,7,8,7,2,1,5
END
```

Note how changing the order of multiplication changes the displayed results:

```
Matrix A x Matrix B
 41  49  58
 26  55  22
 38  73  35

Matrix B x Matrix A
 57  20  42
 96  43  86
 39  17  31
```

You can multiply two matrices of different size if you follow the matrix multiplication rule. You should also be aware that the product matrix has the same number of rows as the first matrix and the same number of columns as the second matrix. The next example program pre-multiplies a matrix B that is 3 x 1 by a matrix A that is 3 x 3. The resulting matrix C is 3 x 1.

```
! Example Program H-4
! Assign values to two matrices of different
! size and  display their product.

DIM A(3, 3), B(3), C(3)
MAT READ A, B
MAT C = A * B
PRINT "Matrix A x Matrix B"
MAT PRINT C;

DATA 2,3,7,5,1,2,6,2,3
DATA 1,2,3
END
```

Note that matrix B is a one-dimensional matrix, sometimes called a *vector* . A one-dimensional matrix can be either a row vector with horizontal elements or a column vector with vertical elements. In this example it must be treated as a column vector for multiplication to be allowed. Here is the result:

```
Matrix A x Matrix B
 29
 13
 19
```

The `MAT PRINT` statement does not display the results in this format but rather as a row vector. You should recognize, however, that the result must be a column vector.

Matrix Division or Inversion

You cannot directly divide one matrix by another but you can achieve the same result by multiplying a matrix by its inverse. Only a *square* matrix — number of rows equals number of columns — can have an inverse. The statement for calculating the inverse is

```
MAT A = Inv(B)
```

Let's use that statement in the following example program:

```
! Example Program H-5
! Multiply a matrix by its inverse
! with formatted output.

DIM A(3, 3), B(3, 3), C(3, 3)
```

```
MAT READ A
PRINT "Matrix A"
MAT PRINT A
MAT B = Inv(A)
PRINT "Matrix B, the inverse of A"
MAT PRINT B
PRINT "Matrix B x Matrix A"
MAT C = B * A
MAT PRINT C

DATA 2,3,7,5,1,2,6,2,3
END
```

Here are the results:

```
Matrix A
 2                    3                    7
 5                    1                    2
 6                    2                    3

Matrix B, the inverse of A
-5.88235e-2        .294118           -5.88235e-2
-.176471          -2.11765            1.82353
 .235294           .823529           -.764706

Matrix B x Matrix A
  1.              4.44089e-15        7.10543e-15
-5.68434e-14      1.                -2.84217e-14
  0               0                  1
```

Some of the values in the product matrix represent very small numbers. These numbers in scientific notation are hard to interpret. Let's look at another version of the program that formats the output:

```
! Example Program H-6
! Multiply a matrix by its inverse
! with formatted output.

DIM A(3, 3), B(3, 3), C(3, 3)
MAT READ A
PRINT "Matrix A"
MAT PRINT using "##  ": A
MAT B = Inv(A)
PRINT "Matrix B, the inverse of A"
MAT PRINT using "Ñ.###  ": B
PRINT "Matrix B x Matrix A"
MAT C = B * A
MAT PRINT using "##  ": C

DATA 2,3,7,5,1,2,6,2,3
END
```

Here is the program output:

```
Matrix A
 2   3   7
 5   1   2
 6   2   3

Matrix B, the inverse of A
-.059      .294    -.059
-.176    -2.118    1.824
 .235      .824    -.765

Matrix B x Matrix A
 0   1   0
-0   1  -0
 0   0   1
```

Now the results look much better, don't they? The minus signs in front of two zeroes are not significant — they indicate that the calculated values are slightly less than zero because computer calculations can have small errors.

The product matrix is called an *identity* matrix — it is the matrix equivalent of the number 1. All values along the *principle diagonal* are one, all off-diagonal values are zero. When a square matrix is multiplied by the identity matrix, the value of the product matrix is the same as that of the original square matrix. It's equivalent to multiplying a number by one.

A Practical Problem

Many engineering problems can be expressed in terms of a set of linear algebraic equations. This set can be rewritten as a single matrix equation that is solved using `MAT` statements. An example is the calculation of loop currents in a resistive electrical network. Consider the case where voltage balance equations of the network are written as follows:

$$R_1I_a + R_2I_b + R_3I_c = V_a$$
$$R_4I_a + R_5I_b + R_6I_c = V_b$$
$$R_7I_a + R_8I_b + R_9I_c = V_c$$

Assume the resistance values are known and the voltages have been measured, and you want to calculate the three currents, I_a, I_b, and I_c. You must then solve the following system of equations:

$$7I_a + 4I_b + 5I_c = 70$$
$$3I_a - 5I_b + 9I_c = 59$$
$$4I_b - 6I_c = 33$$

You can rewrite the left side of the preceding expressions as the product of two matrices — a 3 x 3 matrix of resistances (R) and a 3-element column vector of currents (I). You can rewrite the right side as a 3-element column vector of voltages (V). The matrix equation looks as follows:

```
R x I = V
```

Multiplying each side by the inverse of R and recognizing that Inv(R) (R is the identity matrix, the matrix equation becomes:

```
I = Inv(R) x V
```

Here is a short True BASIC program that calculates the current values:

```
! Example Program H-7
! Solve a set of linear equations.

DIM R(3, 3), I(3), V(3), Rinv(3, 3)
LET Format$ = "--.###  "
MAT READ R, V
PRINT "Matrix R"
MAT PRINT R;
PRINT "Matrix V"
MAT PRINT V;
MAT Rinv = Inv(R)
MAT I = Rinv * V
PRINT "Current Ia is"; Round(I(1),1); "amps."
PRINT "Current Ib is "; Round(I(2),1); "amps."
PRINT "Current Ic is "; Round(I(3),1); "amps."

DATA 7,4,5,3,-5,9,0,4,-6,7.0,12.7,5.3
END
```

The three current values are listed in the program output.

```
Matrix R
 7  4  5
 3 -5  9
 0  4 -6

Matrix V
 7  12.7  5.3

Current Ia is 9.3 amps.
Current Ib is -7.4 amps.
Current Ic is -5.8 amps.
```

The voltage matrix is really a column matrix but the `MAT PRINT` statement displays it in this format. A negative current means that the current is flowing in the opposite direction from the direction you assumed in your network diagram.

Index